VENUS UNMASKED

VENUS UNMASKED

OR

AN INQUIRY INTO THE NATURE AND ORIGIN OF THE

PASSION OF LOVE

Interspersed with Curious and Entertaining
Accounts of Several Modern Amours

A COLLECTION OF EIGHTEENTH-CENTURY BAWDRY
COMPILED BY
LEONARD DE VRIES & PETER FRYER

STEIN AND DAY/*Publishers*/New York

First published in the United States of America by
Stein and Day/*Publishers*, 1967
Introduction, selection and editing of the collection,
Copyright © 1967 Peter Fryer and Leonard de Vries
Library of Congress Catalog Card No. 67-20803
All rights reserved
Printed in Great Britain
Stein and Day/*Publishers*/7 East 48 Street, New York,
N.Y. 10017

CONTENTS

The illustrations are selected from *The Bon Ton Magazine* (1792–5
[1791–6]) and *The Cuckold's Chronicle* (1793)

INTRODUCTION

This anthology is intended to give a fairly representative picture
of the popular sex literature written, read, and enjoyed by our
eighteenth-century ancestors.

The literary prudery which reached its peak in the eighteen-
thirties, and from which we are now finally emerging, began to
gain ground half-way through the eighteenth century and had
become firmly established by about 1771, the year of Smollett's
death. The reasons for the expulsion of explicit sex from serious
literature, and for the accompanying upsurge of verbal taboos,
are not wholly clear. But these changes seem to be associated
with the ascendancy of a middle class bent on self-improvement.
The female members of this increasingly literate class demanded
reading matter free from disturbing sexual realism. A growing
provincial reading public fostered the rise of circulating libra-
ries, which practised censorship. At the same time, the views of
methodists and other reformers about how people should behave
and what they should read became predominant. All these
trends were reinforced, first, by the industrial revolution and its
creation of a new class of factory worker whose reading matter
had to emphasize the benefits of industry and thrift; secondly, by
the French revolution, which sent the middle class to church as
never before and strengthened their revulsion from and fear of
any sort of heterodox behaviour.

By the close of the eighteenth century, this complex of social
causes had produced a marked and unfortunate effect on the
novel, whose authors, though their principal theme was love,
no longer dared so much as hint at what lovers actually did behind
the door of the bridal chamber. From 1770 to at least 1800, for

this and other reasons, the novel was in the doldrums. Richardson, the first English novelist to recognize that a woman's virtue had become a commodity, had been able to entertain his readers in 1740–1 (*Pamela*) and 1747–8 (*Clarissa*) with long-drawn-out accounts of his heroines' bargaining until, after hundreds of pages, each one's commodity (already a common slang term for the female sex organ) was at last appropriated, legally or otherwise, by the villain. By 1800, Richardson and Fielding were too strong for female eyes and Smollett, who had been read aloud in the villages a few decades before, was thought odious because, among other crimes, he called a pisspot by that name. A decade or so later, Scott's 'gay old great aunt' found herself deeply shocked on re-reading the novels of Aphra Behn (1640–89), which sixty years earlier she had heard read aloud for the edification of London Society.

Meanwhile the castration of imaginative literature had been steadily driving eroticism underground, where it would, in the nineteenth century, produce that long line of clandestine pornographic fantasies of which *Memoirs of a Woman of Pleasure* (1749 [1748–9]), commonly known as *Fanny Hill*, was the harbinger. In other words, the overtly erotic was diverted from the main stream of English literature, with dismal effects on both.

These developments are the background against which the present anthology should be read. But they had little direct effect on popular sex literature, whose writers and publishers put up a sturdy resistance to the tide that was running against them, though occasional bursts of legal repression tended to sweep them more and more into clandestinity. They were upholding a good old English tradition, a tradition too firmly rooted to die without a struggle. It never did die, in fact. More or less open publication of mildly bawdy verse and of fairly detached accounts of unorthodox sexual behaviour continued right through the nineteenth century and up to our own day. Almost every decade brought its quota of pamphlets, periodicals, and newspapers, with which the documents in this anthology may profitably be compared: William Dugdale's *The Exquisite* (1842–4), for instance, and *The Day's Doings* (1870–2) and *The Winning Post Annual* (1905-6–23), and *Photo Fun* (1906–9) and its successors. All these combined spicy letterpress with pin-ups of whatever was the fashionable shape. Our enjoyment of reading about other people's goings on, real or imaginary, can be traced back almost to Caxton; so can our appetite for instructive literature which might assuage our sexual anxieties and, possibly, improve our erotic technique; so can our delight in ribald jokes. In *Venus Unmasked* we find these preoccupations of the vulgar as they were reflected in the vulgar literature of the eighteenth century.

There is nothing in this anthology from the pen of a famous novelist: not even the lately celebrated John Cleland. Indeed, it is no accident that only three of the nineteen works here laid under contribution can claim a known author – and none of the three bears its author's name on the title page. For this kind of literature was in general too crude, too ephemeral, sometimes too saucy, for its authors to want any credit for it. It is however worth giving some details of the three authors whose names we do know.

What may be called primitive sexology is represented here by some extracts from one of the many English editions of *The Pleasures of Conjugal-Love Explain'd*. This was a translation of the *Tableau de l'amour considéré dans l'estat du mariage* (Amsterdam, 1687) by Nicolas Venette (1622–98), royal professor of anatomy and surgery at La Rochelle, his birthplace. Venette had studied medicine in Bordeaux and then for three years in Paris, afterwards travelling in Portugal and Italy. It may have been during his visit to the latter country that he came across the vast manual of primitive sexology by Giovanni Benedetto Sinibaldi (1594–1658): *Geneanthropeiae siue de hominis generatione* (Rome, 1642). This work was, in a sense, a codification and justification of the folk sexology of the Middle Ages: those curious superstitions, old wives' tales, folk remedies, and scraps of fact and magic intertwined, which we associate with the names of Albertus Magnus (1193–1280) and Michael Scot or Scott (1175?–1234?), and which go back at least to the medical manuscripts that circulated in the Dark Ages. Present-day writers on sex tend to take a low view of Sinibaldi, whose work is described by Alex Comfort as 'the fount and origin of nearly all the most persistent nonsense about reproductive and sexual matters in the European tradition'. (Sinibaldi insisted, for example, that there was only one 'natural' coital posture, sanctioned by religion.) They take a still harder view of Venette, whose *Tableau* was a popularization of Sinibaldi. Indeed, a colleague of Venette's named Dupuy called it downright plagiarism. This did not prevent Venette's book, published pseudonymously as by 'Salocini, *Vénitien*', from going into numerous editions, or from being translated into German, Dutch and English. The first English edition seems to have appeared in 1703; the third, published in 1712, was entitled *The Mysteries of Conjugal Love Revealed*, Done into English by a Gentleman. This book's immense popularity shows what a hunger existed for sexual knowledge. Whether Venette did more harm than good is an open question; but, to be fair, readers should compare him, not with present-day scientific sexology, but with the legion of twentieth-century popular sexologists. And certainly, Venette came under fire not so much from those who challenged his accuracy as from those who did not hold with sex instruction anyway, and who must have wished that *The Art of Pruning Fruit Trees* (Eng. trans., 1685) had been his only book to acquire fame.

The most polished example of popular sex literature in this anthology is also from the pen of a Frenchman: Jean-François Dreux du Radier (1714–80), a prolific historian, poet, journalist, and translator, whose *Dictionnaire d'amour* was first published at The Hague in 1741. Twelve years later it was translated into English. Dreux du Radier's family intended him to become a magistrate, but he resigned his post as *lieutenant* in the bailiff's court of his native town of Châteauneuf-en-Thymerais, near Chartres, when a relative left him a fairly large fortune which enabled him to devote himself to literature. 'At the bar he was sometimes ridiculous; on Parnassus he was only middling', says one critic. But there is something astringently agreeable about the worldly wisdom assembled in his *Dictionary of Love*: at least, we feel while reading it that these cynical maxims do contain part of the truth about the battle of the sexes, as waged by leisured and comfortably-off men and women in pre-revolutionary France.

The third work by a known author here anthologized is *An Essay upon Improving and Adding, to the Strength of Great-Britain and Ireland, by Fornication, justifying the same from scripture and reason* (1735). The 'young clergyman' to whom this eighteenth-century example of 'new morality' was attributed was called Daniel Maclauchlan. As it happens, we know a little about him and about the reception his book aroused. He was called to the ministry of Ardnamurchan, on the west coast of Scotland, in May 1733. Pretty soon he was accused of intemperate drinking, swearing, and singing indecent songs; but the charges were found not proven and he was duly ordained in September 1734. But in the following year he was imprisoned in the King's Bench prison, London, on suspicion of being the author of the *Essay*. And two years later he was deposed and excommunicated for having deserted his charge from 1 November 1734, 'and travelling to Edinburgh, Glasgow and other places in Scotland, Ireland and England, and writing and publishing a vile, abominable and obscene pamphlet'. On his release from prison he went to Jamaica, where he died before 16 May 1745. His *Essay* had not been too vile or abominable to attract the notice of Scotland's peasant-poet, the ex-barber Allan Ramsay (1686–1758), author of the *Gentle Shepherd* (1725). In his anonymous *Address of Thanks from the Society of Rakes, to the Pious Author of An Essay*, etc (Edinburgh, 1735), Ramsay poked fun in his pawky way both at the 'young clergyman' and at those to whom his honesty had given offence:

> Thanks and Renown be ever thine
> O daring *sensible DIVINE*,
>   Who in a few learn'd Pages,
> Like great *Columbus*, now discovers
> A pleasing Warld to a' young Lovers,
>   Unkend to by-past Ages.

> Down, down, with the *Repenting-Stools*,
> That gart the Younkers look like Fools
>   Before the Congregation;
> Since thou, *learn'd Youth*, of rising Fame,
> *Proves* that there's neither Sin nor Shame
>   In simple Fornication.

> Now Lads laugh a', and take your Wills,
> And scowp around like Tups and Bulls,
>   Have at the bony Lasses:
> For Conscience has nae mair to say,
> Our Clergy-man has clear'd the way,
>   And proven our Fathers Asses. *

* gart – made   Younkers – young men   scowp – leap

11

The rest of *Venus Unmasked* is by authors whose names will never be discovered, even if it were worth while to try. Such knowledge could hardly add to our pleasure in what is essentially, for the most part, folk literature. 'The Jolly Waggoner' and the other verses come from chapbooks – wretchedly printed tales or songbooks hawked by itinerant dealers. The two extracts from *The London-Bawd* (4th edn, 1711) show the clear influence of Boccaccio (1313?–75), refracted through Chaucer and a line of lesser story-tellers. The erotic riddles have a long history in English (and parallels in most other languages). The most polished examples are, curiously enough, the earliest: those to be found in the Exeter Book, dating back to before the tenth century, and composed – or more likely adapted from folk riddles – by some of the higher ecclesiastics of the Anglo-Saxon Church. Love letters like those here reprinted are to be found in a vast number of letter-writers published in the seventeenth and eighteenth centuries. These manuals of preciosity were at first translated or imitated from the French: the letters of Jean-Louis Guez de Balzac (1594–1654) were, in part, translated by William Tirwhyt in 1634; those of Vincent Voiture (1598–1648) by John Davies in 1657; while the original *Academy of Complements* (1640), by 'Philomusus', was based on *La Sécretaire de la cour*, by Jean Puget de La Serre (1600–65). Such translations and adaptations became popular because English middle-class women wished to acquire the graces – the elegant language, refined sentiment, gentility, and pomposity – of the aristocratic ladies at the French court. One wonders how many actual love letters were as stiffly formal and filled with such empty compliments as these models recommend. *The History of the Human Heart*, first published in 1769, is a little-known minor gem of the picaresque. The other pieces, notably the trial reports, the lists of prostitutes, and the fulmination against vice called *Satan's Harvest Home* (1749), speak for themselves. All have their analogues at other periods of our history; but the popular literature of the eighteenth century was outstandingly frank, accepting both the pleasures and perils of sex as part of life.

And here, for the ordinary reader, is what is specially enjoyable about such an anthology as this. We who are entering a period of outspokenness in literature can look back, in these pages, across a century and a half of prudery and censorship and self-censorship to a period when frankness was neither exceptional, nor novel, nor a way of making money. To be sure, life was less attractive in many ways. The eighteenth century was no golden age. Behaviour was cruder and crueller, manners rougher, politeness in the fashionable world a thinner and often cynical veneer. Moreover we are better informed about sexual matters (though much remains to be learnt) and, on the whole, more rational and more tolerant. Nevertheless, where sex is concerned, the eighteenth and twentieth centuries have more in common than either has with the nineteenth. That is why, though there is much in this anthology at which we laugh, our laughter is not unsympathetic. We are discovering an England where the whole of life was of interest to everyone; where a slow-moving rural economy was not yet overshadowed by industrial crises or international tensions; where specialization and alienation had not yet robbed human relations of their directness, mutual responsibility, and charm; where, though deviant behaviour was perennially interesting, no one yet found it either odd or unmentionable that young men sought to give young women a 'green gown' as often as the opportunity arose. To be sure, there were self-appointed moralists, just as there are today, who said it was a dreadful thing, and the country was going to the dogs. But the reign of the guilt-laden and the disturbed, of the professional manufacturers of sexual anxiety, was only just starting by the end of the eighteenth century. Today it is practically over, for the time being. The happy results include the possibility of compiling and publishing an anthology such as this, in which bucolic charm and naïvety rub shoulders with sturdy mercantile common sense, and the matter-of-fact good humour of English bawdy is seen at its best.

Since *Venus Unmasked* is intended for the general reader and not the scholar, no apparatus of notes has been provided. Omissions are unrecorded; obvious errors and inconsistencies have been silently tidied up; eighteenth-century spellings which would not trouble the reader have been retained for the sake of their flavour. The reader who wishes to consult any of the originals, with all their *longueurs*, will find full details in the bibliography. All the works used are in the British Museum, though some of them are in a restricted collection and, for these, special application has to be made. The officials and staff of the British Museum have been most helpful to the compilers, who are extremely grateful.

HIGHGATE, Whit Monday, 1966   P. F.

14

The Fond Mother's

GARLAND,

Composed of several Excellent

NEW SONGS.

THE JOLLY WAGGONER

As I was driving my Waggon one Day,
I met a young Damsel, tight, buxom and gay;
I kindly accosted her with a low Bow,
And I felt my whole Body, I cannot tell how.
Hey gee Dobin, gee ho Dobin, gee gee ho Dobin,
gee ho, gee ho.

I longed to be at her, and gave her a Kiss,
She thought me but civil, nor took it amiss;
I knew no recalling the Minutes were past,
So began to make Hay while the Sun shine did last.
Hey gee Dobin, &c.

I've six Score of Sheep, and each Ram has his Ewe,
And my Cows when they lack, to the Parson's Bull go;
We are made for each other, so prithee comply,
She blush'd, her Eyes twinkl'd, she could not tell why.
O poor Jenny, &c.

I kissed her again, she reply'd with Disdain,
No Kisses I want, prithee take them again;
Then whisper'd me softly, the Weather was hot,
And her mind run on something, she could not tell what.
O poor Jenny, &c.

Then down in my Waggon this Damsel I laid,
But still I kept driving, for Driving's my Trade,
I ruffl'd her Feathers, and tickl'd her Scut,
And I play'd her round Rubbers at two-handed Put.
O brave Roger, *Drive on* Roger, &c.

Her Breasts they were soft and white as new Cream,
And her Motion kept Time with the Bells of my Team,
As her Bubbies went up her plump Buttocks went down
So the wheels seem'd to stand, and the waggon go round.
O brave Roger, &c.

Thus to and again to our Pastime we went,
And my Cards I play'd fairly to *Jenny's* Content,
I worked at her pump till the Sucker was dry,
And then I left pumping, a good Reason why.
    O poor Roger, *broken back'd* Roger, &c.

I thought e'er we parted to have t'other Blow,
When slap went the Waggon Wheel into a Slough,
Which shatter'd her very much out of repair,
Then *Roger's* pump Handle run the Devil knows where,
    O poor Roger, *broken back'd* Roger, &c.

THE ANSWER

As *Robin* was Driving his Waggon along,
The Trees in full Bloom, and the Birds in full Song;
The yellow Corn nodded, and wav'd to and fro,
To his Team he kept Whistling,
    With geehup, geewoa.

A Maid he overtook, and he walk'd by her Side,
The Road was too dusty, he ask'd her to ride,
Then lifted her up, she lay at her Ease,
He begg'd to ligg by her, she said if you please.
    Geehup Robin, &c.

His Waggon he stop'd, and his Leg o'er her laid.
Oh! what are you doing? then whisper'd the Maid,
She struggl'd, she threaten'd, she vow'd she'd begone,
'Till fainter and fainter, she cry'd out, Drive on.
    Drive on Robin, *geeho, geeho.*

He whip'd on his Fore Horse, he jingl'd his Bells,
Such Music ye Eunuchs, your Music excels,
She kept Time to his Tuning, and sigh'd at each Sound,
O dear says she, *Robin*, the Waggon goes round,
    Geehup Robin, *geehup geeho.*

18

She met him half Way with a Kiss and a Squeeze,
And innocently lisp'd out, well, do what you please;
Then softly fell backwards, and bid him go on,
But his Whip Handle broke, and his driving was done,
  Ah poor Robin, *geehup geeho.*

Adzooks, crys *Robin*, my Geer is not right,
But lend me your Hand Lass, I'll set it to right,
With a sweet Compliance she assisted the Swain;
And then he went driving, and driving again,
  With geehup Robin, *geehup geeho.*

THE
London-Bawd:
WITH HER
CHARACTER
AND
LIFE.

Discovering the
Various and Subtile

Intrigues

OF

Lewd Women.

THE FOURTH EDITION.

LONDON, Printed for *John Gwillim*,
near *Sun-Yard*, in *Bishopsgate-street*,
1711.   Price 1 *s.*

HOW A CITIZEN WENT TO A BAWDY-HOUSE
FOR A WHORE, AND THE
BAWD HELPT HIM TO HIS OWN WIFE

A Certain Citizen in *London*, in the late times had a very fine Woman to his Wife, and had but her Vertue been equal to her Wit and Beauty, she might have deserved the first Rank among Women: but Lust had so great an ascendant in her, that her Husband was unable to satisfie her over-strong Desires to the Delights of *Venus*: and therefore having communicated her Thoughts to an old *Bawd* that kept a House of private Entertainment for the Accommodation of Persons of Quality of both Sexes, she told her, that for a Guinea in Hand to her, and two Guineas for the drawing of her Picture, she might be enter'd into her Accademy; whereby (says the *Bawd*) you may both receive the Satisfaction you want, and gain Mony likewise; for the first Charge is all you will be put to, which will be but three Guineas, and ten Shillings to the Attendants, who by the Services they will do you, will very well deserve it. Then she enquir'd of the *Bawd* what the Custom of the House was, and how she must manage herself in that Affair? And then she cou'd the better tell her whether she cou'd order Matters so as to comport therewith.

To this, the *Bawd* return'd this Answer:

I have as genteel a House as most in London, *with several Chambers very well furnish'd for Accommodation of Gentlemen and Ladies; and a Looking-glass in each Chamber so conveniently plac'd, that those who have a mind to't, may see what they do: for some take as much delight in seeing as in doing. My House goes under the Notion of being Let out in Lodgings, and every Gentlewoman that is enter'd, has her Picture drawn, which hangs up in the Dining-Room; where when Gentlemen come, they choose which Person they please by the Picture; and for a Guinea paid to me, they are admitted to her, with whom they make what Bargain they can agree upon. And by this means we are sure that none but Persons of Quality can be admitted; and the Ladies Honours are thereby secur'd.*

21

But for ought I perceive (said the Citizen's Wife) here is constant Attendance requir'd, to be in the way; or else how shall a Gentleman do, that chooses the Picture of a Person that en't there? As to that, replied the *Bawd*, the more any Gentlewoman is there, the better 'tis; and so much the more Mony they get; but those who can't attend always, have their certain Hours; and if a Gentleman has a fancy to such a one, when he knows her Hour, he will come accordingly. – Now you yourself can best judge what Hour will be fittest for you. – That I am at a loss how to resolve, says she. – Tell me how you spend your time all day, says the *Bawd*; and then I'll tell you what you shall do. – Why, says she, many times I rise at five a Clock in the Morning, and having got myself dress'd by six, I go to the Lecture at St *Antholines*, which is done a little before Eight, and then I return home; and at Ten – Hold, says the *Bawd*, you need say no more; there's nothing in the World blinds a Man like a Pretence of Devotion; and therefore if you can get out at Six a Clock to go to the Lecture, 'tis the only time you can take; and by the time the Lecture's done, you may be at home again: nor need you stand much upon Dressing; for if you come in a loose Morning-Gown, you're the fitter for Business.

She lik'd the *Bawd*'s Contrivance very well, and accordingly paid her Entrance-Mony, and deposited two Guineas for the Drawing of her Picture. And in the mean time went constantly to the Lecture every Morning: which her Husband was very well pleas'd at. But her being of late more constant at the Lecture than she us'd to be, caus'd some Suspicion in her Husband, who rising one Morning (which happen'd to be the Day before her Picture was ready) he follow'd her unseen, to know whether she went to the Lecture or no; and she going directly thither, and staying there all the time, her Husband had a mighty Opinion of the Devotion and Piety of his Spouse; and began to blame himself for having entertain'd an ill Thought of her.

All things being now ready at the old *Bawd*'s, and her Picture done to the Life, so great was her Beauty, that she wanted no Customers, each Person that came generally made choice of her to do the Trick with: whereby she not only satisfied her Lustful Desires, but was supplied with Mony likewise, without robbing of her Husband of his Coin, though she wrong'd him more nearly another way; which he not knowing nor believing, thought himself as happy in her, as any Man in *London* was in a Wife: so true is that Proverb, than *What the Eye sees not, the Heart rues not.*

But there were other Citizen's Wives that were as full of Leachery as this, tho' not so handsome; and they found Trading very sensibly decay, since this fair Sinner was enter'd into the College; and she, by her Beauty, having monopoliz'd the topping Customers to her self, was look'd upon with an envious Eye by all the rest; who consulting together, found it was absolutely necessary to give her a remove; but how to do it, was the Question: at last one of 'em told the rest it shou'd be her Province; and she wou'd do it effectually, so as she should never know who hurt her. Upon which, without asking her the Means, they left the matter intirely to her.

The Jilt, to whom the Business was left, was very Witty, but had just but Beauty enough to keep her from being Ugly, and consequently one that suffer'd most by this new *Interloper*; which render'd her so Malicious, that she had rather the whole House shou'd be blown up, than that Upstart shou'd run away with all the Trading: and therefore she writes the following Letter to her Husband.

To Mr *R—d S—n, These:*

SIR,

THO' I never was ambitious of the Honour of being an Informer, yet the Sense I have of the Wrongs you suffer from a Wife that abuses your good Nature, and under a Pretence of Devotion prostitutes her Chastity to every libidinous Stallion, thereby breaking her Marriage-Vow, and dishonouring the Marriage-Bed; has prevail'd with me to let you know so much. And tho' an Information of this kind may perhaps hardly be believed, yet if you will but give your self the Trouble of following her Incognito *every Morning, you may easily satisfie yourself, whether the Account I have given you be true or no: and the better to enable you to detect her in her lewd Practices, when you have seen her Hous'd a little while, you may go in after her; altho' without a particular Recommendation, you will hardly be admitted; and therefore if you please to ask for the Gentlewoman of the House, and tell her you was directed thither by* Tom Stanhop, *to take a Survey of the Ladies in the Dining-Room, she will straight let you see 'em; and after that, you may proceed as you please: and can no longer doubt of the Truth of what I say, if you will but believe your own Eyes. And if you find it so, I am sure you will be satisfied that I have perform'd the Office of,*

Your unknown Friend,

A. B.

This letter she sent by a special Messenger, with order to deliver it only into his own hand, which was done accordingly. But when he had read it, he was so extreamly surpriz'd at such an unexpected piece of Intelligence, that he knew not what to think of it: sometimes he was of opinion, that it was only an Artifice of some that envy'd his Happiness in so Vertuous a Wife, to sow Dissention between 'em; but when he was referr'd to so easie a Tryal, he cou'd not but think there was something more in it than so: upon which he resolv'd to suspend his Judgment till he had made a farther trial. And therefore that Afternoon pretends to have receiv'd a Letter, obliging him to meet a Gentleman the next Morning between four and five a Clock at Westminster, to treat with him about a Parcel of Goods which he was to go and see, and shou'd not be back again till nine a Clock; and in the mean time gets him a very Beautful Suit, Wig, and Hat, and plants 'em at a Friends House, ready to put on in the Morning when he came thither. The next Morning he rises very early, pursuant to his design; and having gone to his Friends House, and accouter'd himself in his new Habiliments, which had so disguis'd him, that even his Friend had much ado to perswade himself 'twas the same Man. In this Garb, about six a Clock, he calls for a Glass of Purl at an Ale-house within sight of his own Door, waiting till his Wife came out; who, as soon as he saw her pass by, pays for his Glass of Purl, and follows her: and she going towards St *Antholin's* Church, he began to think she had been abus'd, and he impos'd upon; but he was quickly convinc'd to the contrary, when he saw her go by the Church, and cross over the way to the Back-side of St *Thomas Apostles*, and there go into a House: after she was gone in, he staid about half a quarter of an hour, and then (according to the directions of his Letter) he went in himself, and ask'd for the Gentlewoman of the House; at which the old *Bawd* appearing, are you the Gentlewoman of the House, Madam, says he? Yes, Sir, says she, for want of a better, I am: pray what wou'd you have with me?

Why, Madam, says he, I want a sort of a Fleshy Convenience, and I'm inform'd you can help me to one: at which the *Bawd* look'd a little strangely upon him; I help you to one, Sir, said she! I hope you don't take me for a *Bawd*; if you do, I assure you, you are come to the wrong House: and I'd have you to know Sir, I'm another sort of Person. *Madam*, reply'd he, if I have offended you, I beg your Pardon; but I was directed hither by *Tom Stanhop*, to take a Survey of the Ladies in the Dining-Room. As soon as the *Bawd* heard him say so, she began to look more pleasingly upon him, and desir'd him to walk up Stairs, and according to his desire had him into the Dining-Room, where he soon espy'd his Wife's Picture drawn to the Life: and making Choice of that, pray, *Madam*, says he, what must I give you for the Enjoyment of this Lady; for she pleases my Eye better than any of the rest? Why truly, Sir, (says she) I have a Guinea for any of 'em; but there's another Gentleman has promis'd to visit that Lady this Morning, and I wonder he isn't come yet; but because I expect him every Minute, I can't recommend any one to her this Morning. Is he with her now, says he? No, Sir, says she, but I don't know how soon he may be: nay, *Madam*, said he, you ought to observe the same Rule here, as in a Barber's Shop, *first come, first serv'd*: come, here's a Guinea and a half for you. This wrought so effectually upon the *Bawd*, that he was immediately conducted to the Chamber where his Wife was: and counterfeiting his Voice, as much as he could; *Madam*, says he, invited by your Shadow, which I saw below, I am now come to be made happy by the Enjoyment of the Substance. To which she answer'd (not knowing 'twas her Husband), Sir, you are very welcome to all the Pleasure I can give you: – what must the Purchase be of so much Happiness, reply'd he to her? To which she straight return'd, I am no Mercenary Person, Sir; nor do I make a Bargain with any one before-hand; but take what Gentlemen are freely pleas'd to give me; to whose Generosity I always leave it: but what you do, do quickly, Sir (continu'd she) for I am limited to such an Hour. Upon which Invitation, the disguis'd Beau fell to, *sans* further Ceremony. And whilst they were a Dancing and Acting the Delights of *Venus*, the Bells of St *Antholin's* Rung very sweetly, which made her say, whilst she was thus encountering her suppos'd Gallant, *O how sweetly St* Antholin's *Bells Ring*! Which she repeated over as oft as they

renew'd their Pleasures. – As soon as they had finish'd their Encounter, her Husband, that he might appear like what he personated, seem'd well satisfy'd, and made her a Present of a Guinea; and so withdrew without Discovery. And she, a short time after, St *Antholin's* Lecture being done, according to her Custom, return'd home, as if she'd only been at her Devotions.

When her Husband had unrigg'd, and put himself in his proper Habit, he return'd home according to the Hour he had appointed, and took no notice of what had pass'd between 'em. But when at Night they went to Bed, he had a mind to try whether he cou'd with the same Briskness manage things at home, as he had done abroad: but finding it on both sides much more dull, he told her, St *Ant'lin's* Bells didn't Ring half so sweetly then as they did i'th' Morning: but however, says he, as long as here it is much cheaper, I like it full as well. His Wife was so confounded at the Words, she knew not what to say at first; nor cou'd she guess how he shou'd know that she had spoke such Words in the Morning: at last she was resolv'd he shou'd explain himself; and therefore ask'd him what he meant by those Expressions – Nay, what did you mean by 'em, says he, when you repeated 'em so often in the Morning? How, says she, in a scornful way, I repeat 'em in the Morning! Yes, *Madam*, says he somewhat angrily, 'twas you repeated 'em in the Morning, when I lay with you at the Bawdy-House, disguis'd like a Gallant, in such a Place, and gave you a Guinea for your Morning's Work. Was it you then, said she, that was with me in the Morning? Yes, Mrs *Impudence*, says he, that it was. Can you talk of being with you in the Morning, without blushing? To what purpose is it to blush, reply'd she, very confidently? For if I do, you can't see it. Nor do I know any reason why you shou'd call me *Impudence*; I am sure I treated you very civilly; and as for my being there, you were there as well as I; and we were both about one Business; and where's the difference then? Besides, I see 'tis your own fault; for if you would be but as brisk at home as you are abroad, I should be very well satisfy'd with your own Performances at home, without going abroad. I see you can do better if you will; and if you don't, blame yourself and not me, if you are made a Cuckold. The contented Man, hearing his Wife's Allegations, promis'd that he wou'd do better for the time to come; and she on that condition promising him to

27

go no more to St *Antholin's* to hear how sweetly the Bells ring, they forgave one another, and were both Friends.

> *Thus Bawds with Wives of Citizens get in,*
> *And then keeps up a publick House of Sin:*
> *And whilst men do maintain their wives so high,*
> *Their Lusts are more than they can satisfie.*

THE
COMPLEAT
ACADEMY
OF
Complements:

CONTAINING

First, Choice Sentences, with Variety of Similitudes, and Comparisons; also the best Complemental Letters.

Second, The Art of Courtship and Genteel Breeding, with Discourses proper for this Ingenious Age, far surpassing any Thing of this Nature.

TOGETHER

With a Collection of the Newest SONGS that are Sung at Court and Play-House

LONDON:

Printed for E. *Tracy*, at the *Three Bibles* on *London Bridge*; And *T. Ballard*, at the *Rising Sun* in *Little-Britain*. 1705.

SONG

A Soldier and a Sailor,
A Tinker and a Taylor,
Had once a doubtful Strife, Sir,
To make a Maid a Wife, Sir,
 whose Name was Buxome *Joan*,
 whose Name etc.

For now the Time was ended,
When she no more intended,
To lick her Lips at Men, Sir,
And gnaw the Sheets in vain, Sir,
 and lie all Night alone,
 and lie etc.

The Soldier swore like Thunder,
He lov'd her more than Plunder,
And shew'd her many a Scar, Sir,
Which he had brought from far, Sir,
 with fighting for her sake,
 with fighting etc.

The Taylor thought to please her,
With offering her his Measure;
The Tinker too with Mettle,
Said he would mend her Kettle,
 and stop up e'ry Leak,
 and stop etc.

But while these Three were prating,
The Sailor slily waiting,
Thought if it came about, Sir,
That they should all fall out, Sir,
 he then might play his part,
 he then etc.

And just e'en as he meant, Sir,
To Logger-heads they went, Sir,
And then he let fly at her,
A Shot 'tween Wind and Water;
 which won this fair Maid's Heart,
 which won etc.

LIST of the SPORTING LADIES.

Miss Rattletrap, from Pall-Mall, London, is calculated for first rates; the rider must be very careful of her, as she starts at *full speed*. Price 15s. *Bank notes* taken, if good, but objects to *paper currency* in general. May be heard of at the bagnio, *Catch-all* Lane.

Miss W . . . S will attend the Races for the first time; at present young in the *concern*, being only fifteen years of age; does business in the *needle* way only after dark – she is very *modest*, and price according to the market. – May be met with near Jericho.

Miss S.D. . . . R, though short, is very handsome, and deserves the attention of those of high rank, as her behaviour is good, and her dress genteel; she will, being *very amorous*, afford the most *pleasing sensations*, at the *critical minute*, to every gentleman inclined for female repast. May be spoken with at the celebrated hotel as above. Price 10s 6d.

Miss D.G . . . Y intends visiting the Races as usual; she is a strapping *wench*, and from her experience and high training, is possessed with every charm to render an *Amour* with her delightful. Her figure is handsome, has good eyes, and a *melodious* voice; is well legg'd and her dress decent. May be spoken with in the Fisher Row. She allows *gin* and *peppermint* in the room, and includes all charges at 10s 6d.

Miss M.G . . . Y still possesses every inviting qualification, though an old campaigner, and her yielding limbs, though beautiful when together, are still more *ravishing* when *separated*; and is mistress of any weight. May be heard of as above, on the same terms.

The two Miss K . . . S will attend the course as usual, being just returned from Windsor; they are quite perfect in the profession of *Wriggle and Twist*, and from the experience they have

had, during their absence from this place, *great pleasure* may be expected by every buck that mounts. They are *pre-eminent* figures, dress genteel, and their behaviour *good*. May be heard of in St Aldate's.

Miss M.W ... E has for some years past been used to the turf, and will keep her accustomed spot; she is short, and rather inclined to be robust, has a good face, and her eyes, at every tell-tale *stroke*, discover her frolicksome wishes for *lechery*. To be spoken with at her standing on the turf, or at the hotel in the Fisher Row. Price according to her customers.

Miss P ... D is a pleasing girl, has a good face, is handsome made, and gives great delight in all her paces. Will only attend this race to take engagements from *billiard table gentlemen*, *gentlemen of the ton*, and *young shopmen*. Price a seven-shilling piece; cautions her customers, as she is acquainted with the *bad ones* in circulation, and of course will reject them. May be seen at the hotel near the *Water Balloon*.

Miss E.P .... R (last from Bath) has been some time in keeping by a *flour* dealer; but by the last *harvest*, and large *imports* of corn, has not received her stated allowance; is therefore obliged, in order to keep up appearances, to do *odd jobs*. Canters well, is perfectly fresh, and will be found a bargain at half a guinea a heat. May be heard of in St Thomas's.

Miss P ... R, sister to the above, a delicate belle of the ton, just arrived from the Continent, as sound as a trout, runs well, and hopes to give satisfaction. As she has, during her residence at Rome, Naples, Italy and France, been frequently hurt by *improper connections* with their rulers, hopes her customers will be very careful in calling on her. Price one guinea.

Marston Nance, of long standing in this town, has been some time in the country for her health, but is returned, for the races only, in prime order; she requires to be used gently, as she is very irritable; and having lately taken fresh instructions in the *pugilistic art*, from the celebrated B ... k and B ... r, at the Frisk, will be apt to treat her customers *roughly* – Gets drunk and is quarrelsome in the evening. – Price 2s 6d. May be met with after dark in St Clement's.

A

RIDDLE:

OF A

Paradoxical CHARACTER

OF AN

Hairy MONSTER,

Often found under *HOLLAND*.

It's such a strange mysterious Thing,
That tho' I've heard a Thousand speak on't;
The wisest Man, God save the King,
Could never yet tell what to make on't.

The SECOND EDITION,

LONDON:

Printed for A. MOORE, near St. Paul's; *and Sold at most of the* Pamphlet-Shops *in* London *and* Westminster. (*Price* 6 d.

A RIDDLE

When full 'tis round, when empty long,
  Sometimes an Hole, sometimes a Slit;
Hairy when old, and bold when young,
  Too wide for some, for others fit.

When tickl'd most, it most will weep,
  And never condescends to laugh;
But pouts and swells, is very deep,
  Extremely pleasant, but unsafe.

'T has Mouth, Lips, Beard, but has no Eyes,
  Nor Teeth, altho' it often bites;
All Day it under Cover lies,
  And chiefly takes its Prey a Nights.

The more 'tis fed, the more it craves,
  Raw Flesh it covets most for Food;
It's lov'd by Fools, abus'd by Knaves,
  Tho' tainted, yet it's held for Good.

The Learn'd, the Wise, the Grave, the Gay,
  In its Embraces take Delight;
Tho' hid, th'adore it in the Day,
  And often kneel to it at Night.

It lies obscurely in a Clift,
  That's fenc'd with Brambles round about;
Yet every Fool can make a Shift,
  Tho' never so dark, to find it out.

When it's best pleas'd it struggles most,
  Is many a gallant Soldier's Bane;
For tho' he makes the homest Thrust,
  It always does the Conquest gain.

The stoutest Man that e'er withstood
  It's pleasing Pow'r, at last comply'd
To sacrifice his purest Blood,
  And then lie panting by its Side.

Tho' Charity be ne'er so cold,
  Most Men are willing to relieve it;
Altho' when fullest it will hold,
  Much more than any one can give it.

If young, altho' it's dress'd in Rags,
  'Twill charm us with its curling Locks,
To run the Risque of greater Plagues,
  Than ever fill'd *Pandora's* Box.

Tho' many a Man this Path has trod,
  And rang'd from Side to Side about;
Yet, none that ever went that Road,
  E'er found its utmost Limits out.

The mighty Prince that rules a Throne,
  Distinguish'd by the Title, King,
For all his Pride, had ne'er been known,
  Had it not been for this poor *Thing*.

It trades for Silver and for Gold,
  And other rich Commodities;
Is very often Bought and Sold,
  Yet ne'er mov'd off the Premises.

It tempts us when we see it not,
  And makes us flatter, whine, and crave;
Yet, when the darling Prize we've got,
  The more it yields, the less we have.

It loves to hoard what others spend,
  With a just generous Intent;
To pay us back at nine Months End,
  With swingeing Interest, what we lent.

Could it but for a longer Space,
    Lengthen the Bliss it lets us taste;
Who would not doat on't? But alas!
    The Joy's too exquisite to last.

Altho' it knows not how to frown,
    It oft torments the Love-sick Heart;
Yet, 'tis the best Physician known,
    To cure the Wounds of *Cupid's* Dart.

Its Ends it loves to gain by Stealth,
    And highly values Youth and Strength;
Tho' it can't judge of Wit or Wealth,
    'Tis skill'd in *Thickness* and in *Length*.

It's such a strange mysterious Thing,
    That tho' I've heard a Thousand speak on't;
This wisest Man, God save the King,
    Could never yet tell what to make on't.

AN
E S S A Y

UPON

IMPROVING and ADDING,

TO THE

STRENGTH

OF

GREAT-BRITAIN and IRELAND,

BY

FORNICATION,

JUSTIFYING

The same from SCRIPTURE and REASON.

By a Young CLERGYMAN.

Omne tulit punctum qui miscuit utile dulci. Hor.

Gen. Chap. i. v. 28. *And God blessed them, and said unto them, Be fruitful, and multiply, and replenish the Earth.* Chap. ix. v. 1. *And God Blessed* Noah *and his Sons, and said unto them, Be fruitful, and multiply, and replenish the Earth.* v. 7. *And you, be ye fruitful, and multiply, bring forth abundantly in the Earth, and multiply therein.*

LONDON:
Printed in the Year M.DCC.XXXV.

FORNICATION JUSTIFIED

All the pretty Ladies may safely venture upon this little, short, substantial Performance. *I took care to put nothing in it, that might Stain their dear, fair Characters. Methinks there is nothing in this* Work, *but what may, by a proper Address, be well enough reconciled to the* firmest Breast, *and tenderest Sentiments. The* whole Piece *will, I hope, be found to slide easily on, in a* regular, lively Motion, *towards the* main End *of it's Formation. I mean, the Support and Welfare of all Societies, and the* mutual Satisfaction *of their* particular Members.

How often may one see a handsome, jolly, sprightly Girl, join'd for Life, to a poor decripit, aukward, silly, sour, ill-natured Fellow, that is not capable of acting his Part to purpose, or giving *due Benevolence* to that pretty Creature, who is so proper a Subject to work upon, and bring forth abundantly? What prodigious Loss is it to Mankind, that so lovely an Object, capable of producing Numbers of wholesome, beautiful Children, should lie idling by this impotent Fumbler.

It's true, those indigent Charmers are sometime supply'd, by squeezing Charity from some young Fellow in the Neighbourhood, whom merciful Providence seems to have ordered there for the speedy Relief of these poor afflicted Widows.

No judicious young Fellow will ever propose to marry, before he is in a Condition to live suitable to his Rank and Station in Life. And a Girl of good Sense will always be very cautious in the Choice of a Husband, as she, very justly, looks upon this as a Matter of the greatest Importance in Life, upon which her Happiness entirely depends. If one, who is very well with respect to his Quality and outward Circumstances, shall make his Addresses to this Girl, it's a great Chance if his Person, Temper, or Humour, is not some how disagreeable. And another that has all the agreeable Qualifications of a Companion for Life, may not have a suitable Fortune.

And if the young Pair don't jump pretty much in their Sentiments, Tempers and Dispositions, it's impossible they can be happy, tho' they should live in the midst of Affluence; whilst they can't share in any other Entertainment, than that of Billing, they are in a fair Way of being for ever miserable. Whilst they have no solid Foundation to support Friendship and mutual Esteem, their Love must drop and fall away of course.

Young Folks that will marry, without any Consideration this Way, may, indeed, pass the Time agreeably enough, in conjugal Caresses, for a few Days; but by the Time the first Heats of Passion are fondly spent in the Marriage-Bed, when the first warm Intercourses of Love are passed, the new Lovers, from the frequent Repetition of their late great Familiarities, generally fall into a languid Indifference, a silly Neglect, and open Contempt of each other.

From such Reflections as these, Ladies and Gentlemen of the best Sense have always looked upon a married State as the last Retreat of Life. They don't incline to venture rashly upon any thing that may possibly be attended with such dangerous Consequence. This puts them under a Necessity of misapplying their first, their ripest Fruits of Love. They can't help throwing aside their rankest Seed into such Places, as they know will not yield any Increase. The elastick Juice springs boldly out, and soon is lost in open Air.

And how is it possible to get this remedied, while Fornication is severely forbid, and thought sinful and dishonourable by Church and State?

But how comes this here sweet, prolific Fornication to have been, of a great while, so unreasonably exploded? Why, if a blooming, young Girl is either offered or prevailed upon to serve a Man in this Shape, for a few Minutes, a few Days, or a few Years; what egregious Stupidity, an unpardonable Sin, should it be, to let slip this noble Opportunity of forwarding that grand Expedition upon which we were, all of us, dispatched into this World? To wit, to multiply and increase. It's not convenient to engage the poor, innocent Thing for Life; but she is ready to please a Gentleman for a little, if he deals kindly by her, and will take care of the Child.

And if a pretty Girl shall be called a Whore, for engaging only for a little Time with a Gentleman in this Way; a Woman that engages with a Man, in the very same Way, until it shall please God to separate them by Death, is, methinks, a much greater Whore; a Whore for Life.

Whore is a naughty Word, which only ought to be applied to those jaded, tough, callous Prostitutes, uncapable of Procreation. Those damned Strumpets, that will ask a Six-Pence of a Gentleman for giving him a most virulent Clap.

If one is foolish enough to venture upon any of these, he is certainly in Danger of Hell-fire.

Marriage has, indeed, of a great while, obtained the Countenance of every Community, as Men have always looked upon it as the best Expedient to prevent that Confusion which must have arisen from the promiscuous Intercourses of the opposite Sexes.

But those fair Ladies, who, rather than lie idle, will *uprightly serve the Lord in their Day and Generation, with Fear and Trembling; with a panting Heart, and aking Limbs.*

I say, if the blessed Fornication of such pretty Rogues as these, was under proper Regulations, so as they should not be put to the Blush for propagating their Kind in this expeditious Way, the whole Nation would soon find their Account in it.

I shall here beg Leave to offer the Publick some broken Hints of a Scheme for regulating these vigorous Intercourses of Love, which presently will appear justified from Scripture and Reason.

I. That in all the Cities, Towns, and Places of Resort in *Great-Britain* and *Ireland*, there should be large Buildings, under proper Regulations, appropriated for nursing young Babies. Where there should be all necessary Conveniences for Women in Child-bearing; handsome Lodgings to be let out to all pretty Ladies that have a Mind to be private and retire from the World for a few Weeks.

II. All Infants whatsoever are to be received into these Colleges, without asking any Questions, and to be taken Care of till they are between six and eight Years of Age.

III. That all these Boys and Girls shall then immediately be ordered to the several Manufactures, and to every other Labour that shall be most beneficial to the Publick: and that they all be engaged, upon proper Conditions, to serve their respective Masters till they are of Age.

Besides a great many other Advantages arising to Society from this new-modeled Charity, we should have an excellent Provision made for all our Foundlings; the want of which, in our Island, is a Grievance that has never, as yet, been redress'd, tho' often lamented by some of our ingenious Writers.

I cannot see how any reasonable Objection can be made, by either Clergymen or Laicks, to this Fornication I now speak of. The one may object that it's frequently forbid in the *New Testament*. The other may think, *it's ruining a great many pretty Girls, as they cannot truely repent of this dear charming bewitching Sin, before they have quite undone their Reputation.*

As to the first Objection; that a Man's Body will be polluted by kissing a good-humoured, sweet-blooded, cleanly, neat Girl, is contrary to common Sense and Experience.

How often do we find our Bodies impregnated with such great Quantities of Seed and animal Spirits, as seize our Hearts, and touch our Brains, to that Degree, we cannot help poring continually upon the fair Objects of our Desire. We are for ever hugging the charming Creatures; putting them in a thousand delightful Shapes and pleasing Circumstances. Our Blood is heated; the Pulse beats high; we are all in a Flame, and can never be cooled, 'till we have dipped into the soft, the sweet, the bubling Fount of Love: and why should the expelling these superfluous Excrements, these agreeably tormenting Humours, by the *Medium* of a pretty Girl, be a greater Sin than evacuating a distended Bladder in the middle of a clean Piss-Pot?

Kissing a sound Girl, a firm Bit, good Flesh and Blood is no where forbid in all the Scriptures; nor, indeed, could a Revelation that breathes so much Benevolence and Good-will towards Men, have ever forbid the Use of these charming Creatures.

If the Scheme I have here laid down should take Place, and meet with kind Reception from the Publick; if they in the more eminent Stations of Life would begin a good Work, and so influence the whole Body of the People, till Fornication was become fashionable, an ordinary mean of recommending us to the World, and so universally applauded, that the most rigid Presbyterian Minister would not blush to be caught making his awkward Addresses to a pretty Girl: we should have all the Bigotry of our keenest Zealots intirely softened, their indiscreet fervours of Religion quite cooled, their Enthusiam diverted and made to flow in another Channel.

Was this happy *Reformation* once brought about, those poor innocent Creatures, that are now neglected and despised for shewing a Readiness to answer the chief End of their Creation, would then be esteemed and regarded by every body as useful Members of the Common-wealth.

And these fair Ladies that are now disgraced, and have their Charms eclipsed for propagating their Kind in the most expeditious Way, should then appear in their full Lustre, and be placed in the most advantagious Point of View, always shining, and darting their kind Glances upon some young Fellow or other. And after they had handsomely acquited themselves of that Capacity, which God was pleased to have bestowed on them for the speedy Increase of his People, when they had spent the Strength and Bloom of their Lives in the Service of their Country, they should then retire from the hurry of Business, commence venerable Matrons, and become the only sanctifyed Abbesses of our holy Religion. All the pretty Ladies would certainly then make their Fortunes instead of undoing their Characters, by this Fornication I have now endeavour'd to recommend unto them.

Whereas these old antiquated Maidens, that Pride, forsooth, in having their Virginity so very long that now they can have no Pleasure in losing it, would be the only Objects of our greatest Abhorrence. These conceited whimsical Haggs, these Monsters of Womenkind, should then be expelled the Common-wealth, or condemned to the hard Labour and common Drudgery of the Nation; in order to purge them of their gross Humours, and clear the Earth of such unnatural Loads.

THE

PLEASURES

OF

Conjugal - LOVE

EXPLAIN'D.

In an ESSAY concerning Human *Generation*.

Done from the *French*, by a Phyſician

Amor Omnibus Idem.

LONDON:
Printed for P. MEIGHAN at *Grays Inn Gate*
in *Holbourn*, T. GRIFFITHS at *Charing
Croſs*, and J. LAPWORTH at the Ano-
dyne Necklace without *Temple-Bar.*
(Price one Shilling.)

OF THE PROPORTION OF PARTS
ACCORDING TO THE LAWS OF
NATURE, AND THEIR DEFECTS

ALTHO' we are loath to Expose the Mysteries of Love to the Eyes of the World, yet 'tis commonly known what passes in Wedlock, and People would still be better satisfy'd to have more perfect Knowledge thereof.

NATURE never made any thing undesignedly, it having establish'd Laws for all the Parts we are compos'd of. Those call'd the *Amorous Parts*, have commonly their Dimension both in Men and Women. The Man's Member according to the same Laws ought not generally speaking to be above Six or Seven Inches in Length, and three or four in Circumference, which is the just Measure, Nature has kept in forming that Part in most Men; if the Virge is longer and bigger 'tis too unwieldy, for which Reason the Inhabitants of the Southern Countries are not so proper for Generation as we.

THE Passages of a Woman's Privy Parts is commonly six or seven Inches deep, the interior Circumference has no determin'd Measure, for by an admirable Structure, this Part proportions so well with a Man's Virge, that it becomes wider and streighter according to the Instruments that touch it.

WHEN the Man's Genitals cannot unite with the Woman's, People commonly accuse the Infirmities of one, or the other Sex. But, for the better comprehending how those Infirmities happen, we must imagine, that the *Intelligence* which is ordered to form the Body of a Boy, in the Mother's Womb, not finding always Matter enough to frame the Genitals, is obliged to render the same Parts defective; and because the Vital Parts are more necessary than those which contribute towards the Propagation of the *Species*, the *Intelligence* sometimes employs all the matter destined to form the Privy Parts of the more necessary ones; and for this Reason, the Privy Parts happen to be very small in time, the Matter being managed for other Purposes.

MORTIFICATION of the Flesh and Chastity, are powerful Causes of the Diminution in those Parts; the Example of *St Martin* convinces us of this Truth, he macerated his Body by unheard Austerities to that degree, and stood up so zealously against the Libertines of his Age, that after his Death, if we believe *Sulpicius*, his Yard was so diminished, that it would hardly have been found if its Situation had not been known.

TOO long or too big Members are neither proper for Copulation, nor Generation, so that for Conveniency a Man's Part ought to be middle sized, and the Woman's Proportionable, in order to a stricter Union, and to receive more agreeable Touches in all its Enjoyments, admitting it true what *Physiognomists* say, *viz.* that Men with big Noses have also stout Members; as also that they are more robust and couragious than others; we have no Reason to wonder at *Heliogabalus's* making Choice of big Nosed Soldiers, that he might be able to undertake great Expeditions with small Numbers, and oppose his Enemy with great Vigour; but at the same time he did not take notice, that well-hung Men are the greatest Blockheads and the most stupid of Mankind.

LITTLE Men have often a bigger Member than others, nay, some Men formerly had Virges of two foot long, if we may credit *Martial.*

BIGNESS and Smallness are not the only Faults, the Yard is also defective when of a little figure, or when all the little Parts it is composed of are not in their right Places; for Marriage being instituted amongst Christians in order to have Children, there is no doubt, but if the Man's Genitals be so ill figured as not to be able to consummate the Marriage; and withal, if this Infirmity be incurable, but that such a Marriage ought to be declared inval'd: in fine, there are so many other Infirmities that deprive the Man's Member of it's ordinary Function, that would require a particular Discourse to describe them all; to be brief, one cannot agreably enjoy a Woman if one hath been rough handled by a virulent *Gonorrhea*, or a *Nodus Virulentus*, if the Privy Parts are Excessive big, if the Yard be bridled by the Filament of the Glans, or lastly, if we are afflicted with any Distempers that hinder caressing, all which have often caused Dissolution of Marriages.

AS for the Women, they are not altogether so hot as Men, they are subject to more Infirmities; Barrenness, which is the most considerable, proceeds sooner from the Wife than the Husband; for if the least Part should be wanting of that infinite Number that is constitutive of the Genitals, Generation cannot be accomplish'd, and a Woman that has such an Imperfection can never hope to obtain the glorious and sweet Title of a Mother.

NO body can guess by viewing the Outside of a pretty and well shap'd Woman, whether she has any Infirmities that may hinder Copulation; but when the Husband goes about to execute the Orders he receiv'd in being married, he meets with Obstacles; the *Hymen* or *Caruncles*, joining close together, and filling up the middle space of the Woman's Privy Parts, frustrate his Efforts; let him push till he is all in a Flame, these Obstacles will not give way to force, even if he were as Vigorous as all the Scholars of the Physician *Aquapeudous*.

THERE are so many Infirmities incident to a Woman's Privy Parts, that hinder the Consummation of Marriage, and consequently Generation, that it should require a Book on purpose to speak of them severally.

AT WHAT AGE A YOUNG MAN AND A
YOUNG WOMAN OUGHT TO MARRY

EVERY Age is not capable of tasting the Sweets of *Matrimony*; the first and last Years have their Obstacles; Children being too feeble and old Men too languishing. The middle Part of our Life is the most proper Age for Venus, who, like Mars, requires only Young People full of Fire, healthy and couragious.

INFANCY and *Puerility* are ignorant as to Production of Men; and tho' some Historians may render this Assertion doubtful, by a Story they make of a Child of seven Years old that got a Woman with Child, yet because there is no Example in Antiquity; and besides that, Generation is altogether incompatible with the Weakness of his Age, one must allow me to stick to my Opinion, and to exclude Children from the Number of those that are capable to engender.

I WILL not say so much of those that have attain'd unto Years of Discretion; for when the Voice changes, and grows bigger and harsher, by the Encrease of the natural Heat in the *Thorax*; when they begin to smell rank, by Reason of disagreeable Vapours that rise from the Seed, when Hair grows on the Privy Parts, and frequent Titilations are felt, then I say a Man may be fired with the Heat of Love, and his Privy Parts dispose themselves for the Caresses of Women.

PHYSICIANS, who narrowly watch Nature, cannot determine exactly the Age Men ought to be of, to copulate and engender, there being so much Variety in the Constitution and Vigour of Men, and the Parts that serve for Generation, that 'tis impossible to decide justly concerning that Affair. One may say general, that we begin to engender at 12 or 14, but we cannot exactly mark out the Year in particular Persons.

WE read in our Observations of Physick, that some Sparks have been Fathers of Children at 10 Years of Age, and some deserve the Name of Mothers at 9.

YET I own these sort of Prodigies is very scarce in the World, and that several Ages may not parallel such a Passage. But the most assured Sign of being in a Condition of engendring is, according to the Sentiments of Physicians, when a Boy can ejaculate Seed, and the Jerins appear in a Girl, then 'tis evident that Nature has furnished one and the other Sex wherewithal to perpetuate themselves. Those Flowing of Humours appear very seldom at 9 or 10 Years; nay, one shall hardly see Girls of 12 and Boys of 14, capable of obeying Love, and to produce such matter as forms Men. A Woman would be very slow, if she was not capable of perpetuating her self, by the Production of a Child at the Age of 16, and a young Man of 18 would be esteem'd very cold, if lying with such a Woman he should find it impossible to partake of the Pleasures of Love. In fine, one may conclude from what I have said, that the most forward Age to get Children is that of Sixteen or Eighteen. Some Physicians have maintained, that Women were hotter than Men, because they are sooner ripe for Business, for if generally speaking, say they, they have more Blood, they have also more Heat, because the natural Heat resides after a more eminent manner, where there is most of that Humour.

THEY add, that we observe Women to be more ingenious and active than Men, because having more Blood they have also more Spirits, which are the Cause of their Activity; they have also sooner Hair on their Privities, and some have been seen to have had their Privities veiled before they have enter'd the Age of Discretion.

THUS Women grow up, and are sooner old, because the

Heat acts upon their Bodies with more strength than fitted for Action, and dissipates sooner their Moistness.

BESIDES, they are much more amorous than Men, and, as Sparrows, do not live long, because they are too hot and too susceptible of Love, so Women last less Time, because they have a devouring Heat that consumes them by Degrees.

THERE are *Messalina's* found to this very day, who, by Reason of their excessive Heat, would be in a condition to dispute with several of the most Vigorous Men; in effect, they suffer Cold with more Constancy, and if their natural Heat, of which they have a large share, did not resist the Coldness of the Winter, we should hear more Women than Men complain of the Rigour of the Season.

PLATO and *Aristotle*, those two great Genius's amongst the Ancients, did not allow to marry before Thirty; and at present, a Body ought not to marry before that time without the Consent of Father and Mother.

THE best is to follow the common Opinion, *viz.* To count a Man perfect at 25, and a Woman at 20, they being then both better qualify'd to marry than in a more advanced Age; for such a Man wants nothing at that Age to content a Woman. His Privities have the Dimensions that are requisite for the well performing amorous Embraces, his Seed is Fertile, the Spirits that ought to serve for Generation are Generated in greater Plenty, and his Virge is always ready to furnish wherewithal to get a Child, even against the will of the Owner. In fine, a Man of a hot and a moist Temperament, that has hot Blood, is Billious and Melancholy, is middle Siz'd, has a big Head, sparkling Eyes, big Nose, wide Mouth, ruddy Cheeks and round Chin, ought to marry so much the sooner. One may say the same is Proportion of a Woman of 20, which cannot live except she enjoys the Pleasures of Love, and follows the Advice the Church gives her in Marrying.

FOR really the Age of 12 or 15 is too tender, to suffer the Yoke of Matrimony. The Persons must be hearty and robust, if they propose any Satisfaction in that State.

WHAT HOUR OF THE DAY OR NIGHT
ONE OUGHT TO KISS ONE'S WIFE

THERE is nothing ruins our Stomach, and weakens Digestion more than Love: it exhausting us to that degree, by dissipating our Natural Heat, and wasting our Spirits, that we feel great Inconveniencies in the principal Parts. But the Brain and Nerves are not the least sharers in the Consequences; their Sufferings have sometime arriv'd to that Point in some Persons, that they have lost their Senses. Allowing therefore *Venus* to be one of the Foreign Causes, most contrary to our Health, when we give our selves up to it, with Excess or out of Season, and on the other hand, as Experience testifies, keeps us in Health, when we use it discreetly: let us examine what Hour of the Day is the most proper to avoid all its Inconveniencies.

'TIS neither the Divertisements of the Day or Night, nor the Pleasure of the Morning or Evening that discompose us; whether it is before or after Sleep we fling our selves in the Arms of a Woman, that does not destroy our Health, nor cause any Weakness in the Stomach and Nerves, nor Heaviness in the Head. All Disorders that arise from embracing of Women, spring chiefly from the Excess of our Passion, and the Ill Husbanding of an Opportunity when we are desirous of Caressing. Were our Passion moderate, our amorous Transports better squared – and if with that we kiss'd, when neither too full nor too empty – I am sure that *Venus* far from doing any hurt, would keep Man in Health; for that which is according to the Laws of Nature, cannot be cause of any Evil, except Abuses happen.

SOME Physicians are of Opinion, that the amorous Pleasures we take in the Day-time, are more destructive than those enjoy'd in the Night; and the Caresses of Women wasting us excessively, we ought to repose, and by Sleep and Tranquility repair the lost Spirits; whereas after our ordinary Occupations of the Day, we undergo a greater fatigue with Women, and tire our selves more by entering upon another wearisome Business.

OTHERS explain themselves better on this Subject, and believe, that Break of Day is the most proper Season for Caressing: they say we are then upon more equal Terms, our Strength not being dissipated by the Actions of the Day; our Stomach not being burthen'd with Aliments; and besides our

Spirits are multiply'd, and natural Heat is fortify'd by Sleep. No troublesome Crudities are felt, Concoction is perfected, and the Nerves being full of Spirits, are not so soon relaxed.

INDEED *Aurora* or the Morning which answers the Spring Season, appears to be more proper for Generation; for after a Man has agreeably diverted himself with his Wife, and taken a little Nap after his Lawful Pleasures, he soon repairs what losses he has had, and quickly cures the weariness he has brought upon himself by Love: then he rises and goeth about his ordinary Concerns, his Wife continuing some while a-bed, to preserve the precious Charge he has entrusted her withal. 'Tis the common Practice of Tradesmen that are in Health, who for the most part have well-shap'd and robust Children. For being tir'd with the fatigue of the preceeding Day, they wait for the Morning to embrace their Wives, and avoid, without doubt, in so doing, the Inconveniencies other Men are subject to, who running headlong without any manner of Reflection, abandon themselves to the violence of their Passion.

ALL Physicians agree, that one ought not to kiss fasting, because one ought not to work when hungry. Work wastes and dries our Spirits, and the Work of Love enervates intirely. To the contrary, we ought to embrace (as some will have it) when our Belly is moderately fill'd; for at such a juncture we feel a strange Desire to be meddling by the Heat and Spirits that the Aliments communicate unto us: after which, we may recruit our Forces by Sleep, Repose being the only Remedy for that kind of Weariness.

BUT to speak freely, all these Opinions are liable to Objections. The Day has nothing that is hurtful, and the Night nothing that is favourable to Love. To the contrary, one may say, that the Evening hath some Attractives which the Night has not. Our Passion awakes, and is rouzed afresh at the Sight of a pretty Person, and the Light of a Taper does not set off Beauty to so much Advantage, as that of the Sun.

OTHERWISE, if we had any thing good in the Stomach, and all Concoctions were not accomplished, the Morning would be the fittest time for embracing. But there being nothing but Phlegm and Crudities in our Stomach at that time, the Remains of our last Meal cannot be stirred by the Feasts of Love but to our disadvantage. By reason of these Crudities, Physicians advise to Eat a little in the Morning, in order to preserve Health, by reason what we have taken being digested, the Stomach will be discharged of the Ordures that are gathered in it during Sleep, and rendred more fit for the Reception of what we shall eat at Dinner.

WHEREFORE if we kiss upon an empty Stomach, we languish immediately, and are very sensible of the Pains and Weakness that such an Evacuation causes. We loose Heat and Spirit by such Caresses, and have no Store within for any speedy Recruits. Nay, far from recruiting, we increase our Losses by the Crudities we have, and constrain them by our passionate Movements to mix with our Blood, and corrupt the whole Mass.

TO resolve the Question therefore, after having proposed what can be said to this matter: I must be allowed to observe neither Day nor Night, Hours nor Moments, but only the Disposition we are in, when Egged on by *Venus*. When perchance we are dull, drowzy by an obscure Pain of the Head, heavy about the Loins, pensive and melancholy without a cause, and withal this have not contrary to our Custom Caressed a long while, we ought neither to observe time nor measures. It signifies nothing to embrace a Woman fasting or full, Morning or Evening. All hours are proper, when the business is to ease our selves of something that is troublesome. There is a Refreshment in change of Business, and the Work of Love is sweeter after our ordinary Occupations of the Day: we find our selves more light and more gay, Digestion is better performed, our Blood circulates more freely: in one word, our Body is not so cumbersome as before.

BUT we must not deceive our selves on these occasions, which happen more rarely than we are aware of; because Nature often eases us of these superfluous Humours during our Sleep, after which there is nothing left to trouble us the next Morning. If we erroneously fancy to be discomposed by too much Seed, when we are out of order upon some other account, we will find the unhappy Effects of it, and scarce be able to attone for the Fault committed.

'TIS better to stay till the first Digestion is over, and the second also accomplish'd, till the Stomach hath discharged what it has digested, and the Heart, Liver and other Sanguine Bowels have changed the Chyle they have lately received into Blood. Then our Body is full of Heat and Spirits; our Stomach has been but now satisfied; our Brains and Nerves are quickened by new Spirits, of which they send a sufficient share to our Privy Parts; insomuch that whatsoever Efforts we make to exhaust our selves, we are supplied from within where-withal to repair Losses.

AFTER these great Maxims grounded on Experience, I dare say, that in 24 Hours there are two considerable Periods for amorous Sports. One is 4 or 5 Hours after Supper. Our Body is then neither too full nor too empty, the Concoction of the Stomach being in some measure accomplished, and the Entrails comforted by the Arrival of new Humours, the Heat is recreated, the Spirits multiplied; and tho' we should dissipate at that time a great many of them, we may have enough left to secure us from many Inconveniences by the Loss. Our Embraces are effectual, and far from feeling of Pain and *Vertigo's* thereby, we are exhilirated and comforted.

WHAT I find most Advantagious in one of these two Opportunities is, that we fortify our selves two several ways. When we Caress a Woman after Dinner, we recruit in some measure our Forces at Supper, and encrease them with Sleep the ensuing Night: whereas, if we kiss after Supper, we have nothing but the Night's Rest to reimburse us of what we are out of Pocket.

BIRDS that follow the Motions of Nature, not to speak here of other Creatures, copulate most commonly in the Evening. We may hear on all sides the Male call its Female in the Month of *May*, and the Female answer the Male. The Heat of the Day having disposed them to Caresses; and the Food they have taken in the Day time heated their Blood, so that the Humour which is Generated in their secret Parts the Night before, excites them to discharge it.

THE greater the Pleasures are, the more pain they cause, if we do not take necessary Precautions to secure our selves from their Allurements.

UNDER this Appearance and Shew of Voluptuousness, lurk frequently Causes of Sorrow and Grief, and we swallow the Poison willingly, without being sensible of what we are about.

WHEN we feel the Darts of Love, and our Heart heated after

a Debauch, as most commonly happens to those that are very Lascivious, we ought at such time to bend all our Endeavours to shun its Incitements, if we are in a Condition to know them. We know that Wine renders us stout and loving, but it stifles also our natural Heat by degrees, when taken to Excess. Indeed we appear more brisk and gay after having taken a Glass, and are fit to undertake more than at another time. A Tree, whereof the Root is heated by Lime, bears Fruit sooner and of better Colour than another, but lives not very long. So Love and Wine acting equal on the Parts, no doubt weaken us in a double Capacity.

WE ought to shun all Opportunities that may incite us to love after a Debauch, if we will avoid the evil Consequences, whereof we are for the most part ignorant.

WHAT Wastings we otherways undergo, joined to the Pleasures taken with a Woman, can but discompose us in a great measure; and I would never advise a Man to embrace his Wife after Bleeding, a Looseness, or some other considerable Distemper, unless he has a Mind to abridge his Days: for *Venus* cannot be agreeable after other Evacuations; let a Man be never so robust, he cannot avoid those grievous Accidents that are procured by irregular Pleasures.

I HAVE known Men, who not being entirely recovered from some acute Distemper, have died presently after Caressing their Wives, notwithstanding there were no Symptoms that might indicate their Death; and at this very time I know some others that will hardly escape.

HOWEVER, if we must commit an Error, 'tis better to do it upon a full than empty Stomach. The Accidence that ensue thereupon are not so dismal, and we have more Remedies for the Succour of Plenitude than for that of Evacuations.

EXPERIENCE has not yet taught us, whether Women ought to observe times in being Caressed. The Humours they avoid when embraced, are not so spiritous as ours, and their Weakness proceeds not so much from the loss of matter, as from the excessive tickling, and the tiresome Motions of Love. But ours are caused by Dissipation of the Spirits, and natural Heat, insomuch that we may say, that Women are in a capacity to do the Trick at all times, but Men ought to take Precautions, as Experience convinces us.

HOW MANY TIMES ONE MAY AMOROUSLY
CARESS ONE'S WIFE IN A NIGHT

VANITY is a Passion natural to Man; he is drawn in when he has the least Thoughts of it, and we may say without enlarging upon the matter, that 'tis one of the greatest Evils, Mortals are subject unto. Really Man is but the Dream of a Shadow, according to a Greek Poet; to consider him nearly, he is nothing but Weakness and Misery, and shews himself most Ridiculous and feeble by his Vanity, and that without doubt made *Democritus* mock Mankind. But Vanity is more particularly exerted in the Matters of Love; to make ourselves admired, we boast of Exploits we never achieved. The Emperor *Proculus* imposes finely upon the World, in a Letter to his Friend *Metianus*, endeavouring to persuade us that he kissed a hundred Virgins, made Prisoners of War, in less than a Fortnight. And the Poet who is the Subject of gallant Conversation, brags of having performed Nine times in a Night.

I OWN we are valiant when we speak of the Feats of Love, but are for the most part errant Cowards, when we should execute its Orders. 'Tis not enough to be wanton with a Woman, there must be something real to show one's Manhood, and be able to produce one of our Species.

I KNOW some are of so Lascivious a Constitution, as to be in a Capacity to kiss several Women for a great many Nights successively, and even be in a Condition to satisfy them; but at the long run, they weaken and enervate themselves to that Degree, that their Seed becomes barren, and their Privy Parts refuse to obey them. *Nero* was not the only Man that wanted Strength and Courage in the Arms of the handsome *Poppaea*, according to *Petronius*. We have a Number of other Examples; and if 'tis allowable to name Persons that have been exhausted and disabled in the Arms of those they have loved, I could fill more than one Page of this Book.

WE ought to look upon as fabulous, what *Crucius* reports of a Servant, that got ten Servant Maids with Child in one Night; as also what *Clemens Alexandrinus* tells us of *Hercules*; who having for the space of 12 or 14 hours laid with 50 *Athenian* Virgins, got the same Number of Boys upon their Bodies, afterwards called *Thespiades*.

WE know, as we have observed somewhere else, that the Seed of Man is kept in Cellules, and little Store-houses, at the Root of the Yard, and that those Magazines resembling small Bladders that communicated the Matter, are ranked as the little Spaces in a Pomgranate, when the Seeds are taken out. There is about 3 or 4 on each *side*, or rather one only that has several small Cavities. These Bladders, as well as the Glandules, are full of Seed in a healthy young Man of a loving Temper, and all may contain so much Seed as is required for 3 or 4 Ejaculations; yet still some remain in the Vessels that come from the Testicles for one more. I am not so exact as those who say, that there are 3 sorts of Seed which have each their particular Virtue. Experience has convinced me, that there is but one sort, which we see sally out from the Virge; and tho' tis found more liquid and thicker in sundry Places; yet mixing when sallying out, they appear but one Matter, and of the same Consistency.

AS soon as the Fancy is touched, and the small Fibres of the Brain shaken by the Thoughts of Love, there is an internal Sweat in our Privy Parts, and the Spirits which rush thither with Precipitation, force out a limpid Liquor of the *Prostate*, which prepares the Conduit for the Passage of the Seed. But when one is join'd amorously to a Woman, then the 3 small Bladders, most ready for Evacuation, empty in an instant, and by so doing give Proofs of perfect Manhood.

MEAN while Nature endeavours to repair the Loss in a Moment, capacitating the Party in a little while to reap fresh Pleasures, and to Evacuate a second time forth Humour as is most disposed to come forth. Nature having no other Aim than Generation in this Action, gathers speedily such Matters as it stands in need of, disposing the Matter to be voided at Pleasure, and the Fancy being perpetually moved by the Beauty and Charms of the Person encompassed with one's Arms, our Passion wakes, and the Privy Parts are still in a Condition to obey. Thus happens a third Encounter with the Woman, and what is most pure and precious is shared with her.

IF we design to go farther, when the Heart is inflamed, tho' the Privy Parts begin to lose their Strength by the Dissipation of the Natural Heat and Spirits, Nature makes another Effort to muster up what Matter is remaining in the *Vesiculae Seminales*, or seminal Bladders, Neighbouring Parts squeezing them on all sides, and preparing the Humour fathered with so much speed for a nimble Ejaculation. Then there is a new Concourse of Spirits, and the Fire which seemed before extinguished, kindles afresh, and is felt in the Privy Parts: where-upon another Evacuation ensues, and the Woman so closely pressed, as to be impregnated by these reiterated Evacuations.

AT last, after having reposed some Time, and by Sleep recruited the dissipated Spirits, we continue still near the beloved Person, and Caresses are reciprocal, tho' they seem then to be somewhat more pressing on the Woman's side, she beginning to be inflamed when the Man is wasted; whereas the Man invited her at first.

AFTER all, there is still some Motion felt, and the Secret Parts, tho' Flaggy but now, begin to Stiffen again, Nature gathering what Seed it possibly can from the Neighbouring Parts, drawing it even from the Testicles to dispose the Party to a fourth Adventure.

I OWN 'tis not done in a Trice, some time being required for Recruiting such Matters as was but now Evacuated; yet of all the Actions in Nature, none is dispatched with greater Celerity and Briskness as Generation.

WHEREFORE the Fancy is once more heated, and neither Courage nor Matter wanting to make a new Sacrifice unto Love. The Secret Parts have Spirits enough to go thro' Stitch, and at the least Caresses of a Woman we perform still, and make her partake of that Humour which she so passionately desires.

BUT if there must be a sixth Attempt, our Parts are cold and languid, and the Humour that comes forth after five several Repetitions is crude and unconcocted, or else a Vermilion of Blood, as that of a Pullet newly kill'd, flowing sometimes in such Plenty, by reason of the Feebleness of the Parts, that 'tis difficult to recover it; instance, a gallant Spark of my Acquaintance, that lives still, but miserably; who having kissed the *Courtizanas* five times in an Afternoon, voided more than two Ounces of Blood the sixth time thro' the Yard.

WHENCE I am apt to believe, and that with some Justice, that all the Efforts we are able to make near a Woman one Night, cannot amount to above 4 or 5 times, these great Extravagancies in Love we are told on, being so many Fables put upon us, that if we did give Credit to People concerning this Matter, without consulting Reason and Experience, we should be the same Bubbles and Fools they are.

THE *Rabbins* aiming only at a the Preservation of their Nation, taxed a Husband's Benevolence to his Wife at the following rate. A Country or Husbandman one Night in a Week; a Tradesman or Carrier one Night in a Month; a Seafaring Man two nights in the Year; and a Student but one Night in two Years. I am sure, that if Women had had a Hand in these Laws, they would not have gone on after that rate. Witness a Councellour's Wife, who told me very ingeniously the other Day, that she would rather be the Country-man's Wife, then be married to all the rest together.

I CANNOT commend the Philosopher *Aeas*, who only kissed his Wife 3 times all the time he was married, altho' she brought him a Son at every time. As for *Xenocrates*, who appeared rather a Stone than a Man, when lying with the *Courtizana Phyrne*, we ought to believe it was the effect of that Continence which was owing to the Study of Philosophy, and not any Faultiness in the Motion of his Secret Parts.

CONSTITUTION, Age, Climate, Season, and our way of Living, influence all our Caresses. A Man of 25 of a hot Complexion, full of Blood and Spirits, who lives in the fertile Plains of *Barbary*, and in easy Circumstances, is better able to kiss a Woman five times a Night in the Month of *April*, than another aged 40 of a cold Constitution, who lives on the barren Mountains of *Sweden*, and gets his Bread with Pain and Difficulty, can once or twice a Night in the Month of *January*.

THE Sensualities of Women are not limited as ours: otherwise the Nobles of *Lithuania* would not permit theirs to have Aid and Assistance from abroad as they do. Truly Women do not feel themselves exhausted, even if they suffer the amorous Attacks of a Multitude of Men successively. Witness the impudent *Messalina*, and the infamous *Cleopatra*. The first having taken upon her self the Name of *Lyioca*, a famous *Roman* Whore, out did in 24 Hours in a publick Stew a Harlot, that was esteemed the very bravest in Love, by 25 Feats. The other, if we believe a Letter of Mark Antony, one of her Gallants, underwent in one Night's Time, the amorous Efforts of 106 Men, without appearing in the least Fatigu'd.

WHETHER THE MAN FEELS MORE PLEASURE
IN ENJOYMENT THAN THE WOMAN

THERE is no Pleasure swifter or greater than that of Love, it exhilirating all the Body in an instant, and filling the Soul with Transport. We need no Instructions, nor means to learn to Love, Nature having implanted in our Hearts something, I do not know what, of loving, which is cultivated by degrees as we grow up, and when it incites us to Caress a Woman, 'tis hardly expressible how many ways there are to please us; the Approaches of Love being as delicious as the Enjoyment it self. The Pain we suffer in loving, pleases before the Pleasure it self. In short, all the Passions of the Soul are, in a manner, Slaves to this Amorous Passion.

I CANNOT be perswaded a Man of Sense would take Pleasure in so often repenting, if Nature had not placed excessive Delights in the Action of Love. But the flattering of Love being so engaging, 'tis impossible to be secur'd from their Snares. The Pleasures taken in Woman's Company much needs be great, since Devils, according to Divines, love them so much.

BOTH Man and Woman taste excessive Pleasures in mutual Caresses, and 'tis difficult for me to determine which receives the most. Yet seeing we may discover which of the two has the most sensible and twisted Genitals, engenders most Wind, has the strongest Fancy, hottest and most fluid Blood, I am apt to believe the Question may easily be decided.

NO doubt but our Privy Parts are more sensible than those of Women, being all nervous, or to explain my self better, nothing but Nerves, whereas the Women's Parts are fleshy, and consequently less sensible. If amongst all the Parts of our body, the Nerves feel the quickest Pain when they are touched, they must also receive the greatest Pleasure. Besides, our Spermatick Vessels, thro' which the Seed passeth, are extreamly twined and twisted, and our Testicles, properly speaking, only a Contexture of Nerves and Vessels folded one under another; that could we untwist the Spermatick Vessels, and afterwards measure them, I should not tell a Lye in saying, that they are Eight or ten Times longer than we are tall; whereas those of Women are not longer than a Finger.

WINDS being necessary for the Pleasures of Love, we must

own, that as Men are more irregular in their way of Living than Women, they Engender also a great deal more Winds and flatuous Spirits.

WE have also a firmer Mind, and stronger Fancy, than Women. The Filaments of our Brain are more stretched and hard, and when we Love, 'tis with greater Force and Spirit. Women to the contrary are of a more inconstant Mind, and weaker Fancy. The fibres of the Brain are softer, and more flexible; and tho' they appear sometimes to Love more ardently, yet they do not feel so much Pleasure in Caresses as we.

IN fine, our Blood is sharper and hotter than theirs, being agitated with more Force; and some Men will shake with Cold at the Approach of a Woman they have a mind to embrace; the Heart and Brain, sending at such a time, the greatest Part of the [Heat and Spirits with Precipitation to the genital Parts.

WHEN the Seed swoln with Spirits makes its Passage thro' our twisted Vessels, we are drunk with Joy. The hot and trickling Vapors that arise from it, and the precipitate Motion of the Spirits that penetrate the Membranes, contributing not a little to these Sensualities.

ALTHO' Women are touched to the Quick by the Pleasures of Love, when we Embrace them; yet I cannot believe, that their Sensibility is so great as ours; their Seed being liquid and less hot, is not filled with so many Spirits, and does not sally out with that Swiftness as ours.

INDEED, we may say, that the Genitals of Women are agitated with more violence, when they desire to be moistened by the Man's Seed, and that they feel greater Pleasure when their Parts draw, and suck out Humours for Conception; besides, seeing they waste by considerable Evacuations, some have been induced to affirm boldly, that the Pleasure of Women surpasseth by one-third, that of Men.

WHETHER THE WOMEN ARE MORE
CONSTANT IN LOVE THAN MEN AND WHY

SOLOMON the wisest of Men, who knew Women better than we, compares them to the Wind; and speaks much to the Purpose in saying, *that he that has a Woman in his Possession, and endeavours to keep her to himself, is like unto him that will retain the Wind with his Arms.* Indeed Women are naturally very fickle, and easily carried by small frivolous Matters through the Weakness of their Judgement. They delight in Trifles, and spend all their Life-time in giving Proofs of the Inconstancy of their Sex; their Stature is small, their Strength indifferent, their Actions languishing: in one Word, they are weaker and more inconstant than Men.

MEN, to the contrary, are lustier, more vigorous, and more active; they have better Conceits, and argue with more strength; they are more firm and resolute in their Business, more constant in their Undertakings, and bolder in their Actions; their Constitution being hotter, dryer and stronger: 'tis without doubt for this Reason, that the Scriptures allow them the Superiority over the Women, and to be Lords and Masters of the Family.

LOVE is such a waggish and violent Passion, that its Excess is more commonly observ'd in little than great Souls. I own no body is exempted from its Empire; but to speak the Truth, *the weakest go to the Wall* in this Passion; of which Number Women are. And Perseverance being a Quality inseparable from Love, we may conclude, that Women love longer, and are more constant in their Love than we are; for Love ceases when we discontinue it; and there must be real Love to Authorize one to say, that one loves.

IF we observe what passes daily in the World, we may be convinc'd of this Truth; experience teaching us, that the Modesty of Women hinders them from flying out, and at the same time obliges them to love such only as they are allow'd to be free withal. Besides, Modesty is a certain shame, that keeps them in their Duty, and renders them constant against their own Will. I must say the same of that Fearfulness, which commonly accompanies the fair Sex. Reservedness also, which is so natural to Womankind, comes not far from Constancy; and one may say, that it is its inseparable Companion.

MOREOVER there are few Women but what love those desperately that obtain the first Favours from them. They are so ty'd to their first Lover, that if by some great Consideration they are oblig'd to be ally'd to others, they still preserve some

Tenderness in their Heart for him that had the Flower of their Virginity.

BESIDES, we know they are more sedentary, and less proper for Business than we; and that Solitude, and looking after House-keeping, withholds them from Company, that they have not so many Opportunities to be false as we.

LASTLY, the Law retains them, by punishing severely such as are loose, condemning them to be shaved, and thrown in a Monastery, for being too inconstant in Love.

IF we reflect on our Constitution and Inclinations which are derived from it, we may be convinced, that Love does not tyrannize over us to that Degree as over Women. We are embarrased by Multiplicity of Business, and to divert our selves, we fall in with the first Play-Toy we meet with; our great Heat emboldening us to make new Conquests. We make sure of the first that comes in our way, and for the most part satisfy our selves when Opportunity favours. Our Mind is too free to be subject to a tyrannick Constancy, and being disgusted with one Person, we are prompted to change our Diversion. She that pleases one Week, displeases another; and the little Petts that happen in the Caresses of one, are soon changed into new hopes for another. We are apt to believe, that new Pleasures are of a different Nature from the past, and our natural Inconstancy is fomented by false Insinuations, and alluring Hopes.

MOREOVER, Men feel greater Pleasure, and waste more than Women; and as their Disgusts are more insupportable, and better grounded, the God of Love lays wait to extend his Empire, by insinuating Persuasions, that change is far more agreeable and voluptuous than Constancy; and we are so simple, notwithstanding our Experience to the contrary, as to be cowardly led away by these secret Persuasions and hidden Motions.

A CERTAIN Woman said, very wittily, *that she earnestly desired the Caresses of several Men, because she was a reasonable Creature*; Whence one may infer, that Men having a stronger Reason than Women, they may make use of it upon the same Terms and Conditions. The most reasonable People are exposed to the Softness of Love; and it being natural to all the World, there are few than can escape its Attractives. But excessive Love being a Distemper common to both Sexes, those that have great Strength of Mind resist its Tyranny more couragiously, and though sometimes smitten, change Objects to avoid the Alarms and Inconveniences it causes; whereas little Souls are not able to resist those secret Motions; besides being more fearful, they are cowardly led away thro' the Weakness of their Condition, and always continue ty'd to one Person.

IT being true therefore, as Experience itself witnesseth, that Men cannot long subject themselves to the Empire of Love, and that their Flights and Sallies are only the Effects of its secret Inspirations, we may conclude, that they are much more inconstant in Love than Women.

PASSIONS then being natural to Man, and Jealousy, one of the most violent, and in the Scriptures compared to Death and Hell, it will never forsake him; and as it is derived from Love, we may reasonably believe that all Lovers are jealous, which we design to prove in this Discourse.

THE Soul, troubled by divers Passions, endeavours by all means to disengage it self from its Doubts. Curiosity prompting it to examine all the Circumstances of the Business, it spies and observes narrowly the beloved Object for fear of losing it; but this extravagant Enquiry augments its evil, and instead of curing, causes a Mortification and Gangreen.

REVENGE mixes with Jealousy, and to have the Satisfaction of letting the World know a Wife's Weakness by discovering her amorous Secret, Men draw the Laughter and Scorn of all the World upon themselves, and a perpetual Stain on their Reputation.

BUT the Soul not being ignorant, that all that is in the World is subject to Changes, it begins to fear the Loss of what makes its Happiness and Satisfaction, and is afraid it may fall to another's Share to enjoy it. This Fear we call properly Jealousie, which owns Love for its Father and cannot refuse Fearfulness for its Mother. 'Tis strange, that the Inclinations which cement Friendship in the Commerce of Men, should prove the Cause of Hatred in excessive Love.

JEALOUSIE has such Power and Influence upon some Men's minds, that according to the report of *Tertullian*, some have feared their Wives would be stoln from them at the least Gust of Wind, or if perchance a Mouse should pass by their Chamber Door.

A FEEBLE Mind is no sooner seiz'd with this Fear, but Hatred finds a place also; but Love being not yet entirely banished, strange Disorders happen by such opposite Passions; and the Soul's not being destroyed, is to be Attributed to the Number of its Enemies. On one hand, Hatred freezes the Heart, the principal Seat of the Soul, stifles the Spirits and Heat. Poor Heart! How dost thou suffer by this monstrous Passion? Anger, Grief, and Perfidiousness are derived from these contrary Passions as also Hope, Despair, Joy, Sadness, Fury, Rage; and lastly, a desire to be reveng'd even to the hazard of Life and Reputation. Some have extended their Jealousie beyond this Life, as the King of *Morocco*, who being defeated in War, envyed Mankind the Enjoyment of his Wife after his Death; wherefore putting her upon a Crupper behind himself, and spurring his Horse, he fell from the Precipice of a Mountain, as *John of Leon* informs us.

NOTHING being hidden in this World, Vengeance breaks out sooner or latter; scandal arises, and a hidden Crime is often punished so as to extend its Misfortunes to an innocent Posterity. Perhaps a jealous Person comes to know himself when the Distemper is form'd and not quite past cure, yet he meets with Grief and Repentance for his Pains, the Effects of an irregular Love and the End of Jealousie; for Jealousie is never without Love; and as desire of Life accompanies all sick People, and Grief never touches the Dead, so Jealousie never abandons those that are in Love, but is never met with in the cold and indifferent.

THE Fear of losing what is beloved is stronger in a Woman's Fancy than in a Man's; and tho' Women are naturally timid, yet we see by Experience, that when jealous, they are bold and intrepid to that Degree, as to undertake the Perpetration of a Crime sooner than we, if it comes to that point.

MOREOVER, a Woman being naturally weaker, and consequently more needful of the Help and Support of a Man, is also in a greater fear of losing him, when she loves him well.

ON the other hand, being more constant in Love than we, as we have proved it in the foregoing Chapter, she receives more Impressions by the Motions of Love and Jealousie.

BESIDES, Lasciviousness being a Powerful Motive of this Passion, and they being more troubled therewith than we, are also more jealous. She'll think her Husband has not enough for her, and in this lascivious Thought be afraid that another shares those Pleasures with her, which she desires to her self, and Fancies to be her Right.

FURTHERMORE, she is oftner angry, and continues longer so than a Man; at which time Jealousie turning into Fury, renders her fit for the blackest Enterprizes in the World.

LASTLY, there is no Savage Beast more cruel than a Woman disorder'd with Jealousie. We need no other Proof than *Medea*, who kill'd her own Children to be reveng'd on her Husband.

MEN proceed almost after the same manner, bating that Lasciviousness has not so great a share in their Jealousie as in Womens. They only fear another may ravish what they fancy belongs to themselves; and in this black thought load their Soul with the most cruel Passion in the World.

IN effect such People resemble Stags, which being naturally very fearful, are extreamly jealous of their Hinds.

I'LL conclude then, that Love is never without Jealousie, and that no Body can Love without being Jealous.

THE

DICTIONARY

OF

LOVE.

In which is contained,

The EXPLANATION of moſt of the
Terms uſed in that Language.

LONDON:

Printed for R. GRIFFITHS, at the *Dunciad*
in *St. Paul's Church-Yard.*
M.DCC.LIII.

ABSENCE

How dear is my absence from you going to cost me? How tedious will the hours seem?

This signifies precisely, 'If I was always with you, my stock of fine speeches would be soon exhausted: I should have nothing new to say to you: when I see you again, you will like me the better.'

Some rhyming fools are fond of the occasion of complaining, in lamentable verse, of the tortures they suffer by absence; which is, however, only a handle of shewing their wit, at the grievous experience of truth and reason, which they martyrize in the stale, trite hyperboles of hours being months, months years, and years whole ages, in their kalendar: of their being kept alive only by the hopes of seeing what they love again. These strains are proof of the real absence of common sense.

To ABUSE, *to encroach, to misproceed*

This term is often used in protestations, and generally tacked to a negative. *No! I will never abuse your goodness.* Or *without the negation*, in a more emphatic strain: 'I ever abuse your goodness!' *Heavens forbid!* All this signifies, purely and simply, 'since you will have promises and protestations, to bring you to my ends, there they are for you.'

Sometimes it is used in the following case, with great art and delicacy. Thus, when a lady grants a slight favour, as a kiss of her hand, perhaps even of her mouth, and the lover, who is never to be satisfied, proceeds on such encouragement to liberties that put decency in danger; the lady, naturally alarmed, chides the encroacher. *I am too good-natured. – I own*, replies the sly lover, *I abuse your good-nature; but, with so much love as I have, 'tis impossible to have discretion.* This confession, that he *abuses* her goodness, carries with it such an air of candour, that it is hard not to forgive him, with respect, or check his forwardness. It is as much as to say, 'let us see whether you are a novice or not? Whether you have duly taken your degrees of assurance? Or whether you are not in your horn-book of gallantry?'

ADDRESS
You address yourself to the wrong person, I assure you.

This little affectation means at bottom, that one is not sorry to have a lover, but that it is necessary to put on an air of dignity; to remind him of one's value; to give the spurs, whilst one reins in the bridle.

However, these finesses of love-rhetoric over-awe none but fresh-water adventurers: and that terrible expression, *to whom do you think you are addressing yourself?* is oftener a trap for a compliment, than a denotation of anger.

ADVANCES
When these are made on the woman's side, they either suppose an excessive superiority, or an excessive love.

A woman who has made advances, never remembers them without rage, unless she has reason to remember them with pleasure.

ADVENTURES
Adventures in gallantry begin to lose much of their relish, by the want of their former seasoning, fears and dangers. Assignations are now so easily made, that a man must know little of the world, who thinks there is any need of a masquerade to make them at. It is just as insignificant, and as much out of use, as rope-ladders or long cloaks.

BEAUTY
A modern author calls it, a bait, that as often catches the fisher as the fish. One of the best baits to catch a woman, is to persuade her that you are intimately persuaded of her beauty. Such is the powerful influence of this branch of flattery, that rarely does that woman refuse the man any thing, to whom she has been weak or vain enough to listen to his praises upon this chapter. On the other side, she never forgives those, who, she has reason to think, look on her as disagreeable, or ugly. In short, with women themselves, their first merit is that of beauty; which they would lay less stress upon, if they were to consider how short a time they have to enjoy it; and how long an one to be without it.

An author, without considering how arbitrary the idea of beauty is, has given the following detail of the capital points of it; in which every one will make what alteration his own taste may suggest to him.

1. Youth.
2. Stature, neither too high nor too low.
3. Neither too fat nor too lean.
4. The symmetry and proportion of all parts.
5. Long hair, or prettily curled, fine and silky soft.
6. The skin smooth, delicate, and of a fine grain.
7. Lively white and red.
8. A smooth high forehead.
9. The temples not sunk in.
10. The eye-brows in arcade, like two lines.
11. The eyes blue, their orbits well-fashioned, and turned to sweetness.
12. The nose rather long than short.
13. The cheeks, rounding away in softened profile, and dimpled.
14. An agreeable smile.
15. Two lips, pouting, of the coral hue.
16. A small mouth.
17. Teeth, pearly white, even and well set.
18. The chin rather round, plump, and ending with a dimple.
19. The ears small, and close to the head.
20. A neck of ivory.
21. A breast of alabaster.
22. Two balls of snow, firm, self-sustained, and deliciously distanced.
23. A white hand, plump and long.
24. Fingers tapering.
25. Nails of mother-a-pearl, and oval-formed.
26. A sweet breath.
27. An agreeable voice.
28. A free, unaffected air and carriage.
29. The shape noble, easy, and disengaged.
30. A modest gait and deportment.

BOLDNESS

Excuse my boldness: This, when said in the instant of snatching small favours, means, 'I am sounding the channel, to see how

you will take small liberties: if you excuse this, I shall have room, I hope, to proceed to greater.'

There are few women who would not sooner forgive an excess of boldness, than an excess of timidity.

FAITHFUL

A faithful lover is a character greatly out of date, and rarely now used but to adorn some romantic novel, or for a flourish on the stage. He passes now for a man of little merit, or one who knows nothing of the world.

By *faithfulness*, then, is to be understood a firm resolution of reducing an obstinate fair-one; and by a *faithful lover*, one who has not yet gained his point. The last favours are the *extreme unction* to love, which rarely or never survives their administration.

FATE,
Destiny, Stars, etc.

How can a poor creature help her fate? This signifies that the fair-one is too resigned to the system of fatality, to pretend to stem the force of a passion that borrows the plea of it, and is hurried down the stream; whilst the term serves her to yield honourably, and makes a sort of decent figure in a letter or speech.

FAULTS

The person one loves never has any. Either the lover does not see them, or is as much reconciled to them as to his own. If they offend him, he is so far from being a true lover, that he is scarce more than an acquaintance, and less than a friend.

FAVOURS

All that a mistress grants to her lover is called so.

They magnify or lessen the favours according to the exigence of the case: but, generally speaking, a lover magnifies small favours, and lessens the great ones. Thus, when he pretends to exalt a trifling favour he has obtained, it is by way of insinuation how grateful he would be for greater ones, and thereby inspires the fair-one with a mind to try him with them.

When a lover lessens a great favour, all he says to that purpose signifies, 'if I was to form to you too high an image of the favour I am soliciting, you would think twice before you granted it me.'

The *last favour* is so called with great propriety; it being out of a woman's power, after that, to grant another; she then commences the person favoured, not favouring.

HUSBAND

What is a Husband? Hear a lady's definition, who composed a vocabulary to express the character of one, from her own experience, and which proves how copious our language is on that article. He is, said she, a snarling, crusty, sullen, testy, forward, cross, gruff, moody, crabbed, snappish, tart, splenetic, surly, brutish, fierce, dry, morose, waspish, currish, boorish, fretful, peevish, huffish, sulky, touchy, fractious, rugged, blustering, captious, ill-natured, rusty, churlish, growling, maundering, uppish, stern, grating, frumpish, humoursome, envious dog in a manger, who neither eats himself, nor lets others eat.

To JEST

When at a *Tête-à-tête*, a lady says, with a certain air, *I do not like this jesting*, it signifies, 'everything declares in your favour; even this little coyness is but a signal of your victory'.

Other more learned interpreters pretend with more boldness and probability, that these words mean, 'this is no time for jesting: I should like better you was in earnest'. And that it is using a lady very ill not to take it in that sense.

Some make love only by way of jest, but this is inhuman sport: they may as well commit murther in jest.

KISS

Some authors will have it, that a kiss is no kiss, or at best a half one, unless returned at the same time.

In some countries there is such a stress laid upon it, that a woman who grants a kiss, has passed away all right to refuse any thing else. It is the seal of a treaty of surrender at discretion.

In ours, its signification is determined by the circumstances,

the degree of warmth, the part, the time, and other particulars needless to enumerate. But of all kisses, the turtle-billing one is the most emphatic, but rarely used, where there is not fully liberty to use everything else.

In general, however, one may venture to pronounce kissing dangerous. A spark of fire has often been struck out of the collison of lips, that has blown up the whole magazine of virtue.

KNEELING

Women are not absolutely in the wrong to take themselves for little divinities, when they see this tribute of adoration paid them. And they are the only sublunary beings to whom it may be paid without humiliation.

It is a posture, however, that ought to put them on their guard; for it is a devilish favourable one to the enterprises of a lover. It is an attitude invented to prove respect, and which is often very commodious for the breaking it.

LEVEL
Love levels everything

This is a shrewd persuasive turn, often employed by a lover of a superior rank to a mistress of an inferior one, to induce her to conceive chimerical hopes, and stun her reflections upon the consequences of the sly sap they serve him to carry on. Sometimes he joins to it the examples of some famous fools, who have thrown themselves away upon *Pamelas*, and winds up with some insidious praises of the beauty and merit of the person upon whom he is designing. This conclusion is generally very forcible: but before she determines, she would do well to consult, upon the value of it, one of those numberless deserted damsels who have been the dupes of their hopes from it.

To LOVE

In times of yore, signified an invincible inclination: at present it has quite another meaning, and often no meaning at all. There is as much difference between what we call *Love*, and what our fore-fathers called so, as between our dress and theirs; between our snug frocks and cut bobs, and their slashed doublets and natural hair. Every sublunary thing changes; but our manner is so easy and commodious, that it threatens a long duration.

Most of the present Love is what our blunt ancestors called by another very coarse name, or what is infinitely coarser yet, though unblushingly pronounced, Sordid Interest.

Tom Featherhead loves Miss Lightairs. That is to say, Tom is a coxcomb, whose glitter has dazzled the eyes of a silly frothy girl: he is what is called extremely well with her, and has the rare privilege of murdering his time in gallanting her to Ranelagh, Vaux-hall, etc., charmed with which glorious reputation, he would not change it for a Marlborough's or Turenne's.

Goatly loves the innocent Sylvia. That is as much as to say, he is laying every scheme he can imagine, to add her to the list of the wretched victims who have fallen a prey to his brutal appetites: whilst all her personal beauties, her inimitable bloom, her fine-turned shape, have been surveyed by him, with the same eye as Cannibals view their captives, of whom they design to make a meal.

When young Sharply says to the old liquorish Lady Wishfort, *I love you*, the true English of this is, 'I am a younger son, unfortunately born under a star that gave me the soul of a prince, and the fortune of a beggar. Let us supply one another's wants.'

LOVE
The Love-passion

It is a modern discovery, that Love is as much a bodily appetite as hunger and thirst, which are removed by a hearty meal, or a copious draught; and, like them too, is liable to a surfeit. This doctrine is so far countenanced, that some knowing ladies prefer by much, that Love which is a corporeal want, to that which is an imaginary one. – Some indeed will have it a distemper, that may be cured by plentiful evacuations, bleeding, purging, and a low diet. A certain duke, who was what they call violently in love, being seized by a fever, for which he was bled, blistered, and brought low in the flesh, on his recovery he lost at once his fever and his love, to a point, that no trace of it remained in his imagination.

As to Platonic Love, it is a mere opera-singer, a voice, and nothing more. Lady Manlove, who is an excellent judge, said, if such a rascal as *Platonic Love* was to come within her doors, she would order her porter to kick him out.

NO

Is a term very frequently employed by the fair, when they mean nothing less than a negative. Their *yes* is always *yes*, but their *no* is not always *no*. The air and tone of it determines the signification: sometimes too the circumstances, a smile, or a look.

PRESENTS

A term of great power and energy, and, generally speaking, the shortest way for a lover to get to his journey's end. They are proportioned to the fortune and rank of the person upon whom the design is. A duchess may fall to a diamond necklace, and a chamber-maid to a taudry ribbon. It has even been known, that a silly girl has been reduced by a dozen of stick-cherries. In short, the great art is how to adapt, place, proportion, and time them.

PROVOCATIVES

There are no provocatives like youth and beauty on one side, and a healthy constitution on the other. It is all over with a man, when he is to be indebted for his powers of enjoyment to Spanish-flies, or inflammatory food; when he is obliged to cry out with the worn-out lecher.

Give me, ye Gods! of strength, those rich supplies,
Eggs, oysters, jellies, soups, and sparrow-pies!

PRUDE

Signifies a woman who at her heart is no enemy to gallantry, but loves it without noise; or one who is slenderly provided with personal charms, and betakes herself to prudery, to acquire the esteem of the world; or one who wants to throw the veil of it over her conduct, or use it for a varnish to her reputation.

These grimaces, however, deceive nobody. We are in too clear-sighted an age to be the dupes of that false delicacy, that takes umbrage at everything, and gives a criminal sense to the most innocent actions and words; a mysterious severity, of which some women hoist the standard, and pass one half of their lives in concealing the other half.

RESPECT

True love never goes without respect: and its counterfeit is often obliged to feign it, till an occasion serves to throw it out of the windows.

I have too much respect for you, in the mouth of a sly prostrate engineer, signifies, 'I know better things than to hazard freedoms, prematurely, before the way is cleared for them.'

In the mouth of a novice, it means, 'I have too much bashfulness.'

There are occasions, in which the plain English of it is, 'I despise you too much to tell you that I love you.' And this is generally addressed to those figures made to inspire rather a prudential respect, than rude desires.

Cruel is the situation of a woman treated with a respect, for which she is forced to blush, by the consciousness of neither deserving, nor desiring it.

To RUIN a woman, to rob her of her honour, or (what is worse to many of them) of the reputation of it.

Terrible as this word sounds, there are of them, who would look on no unhappiness so great, as that of having no reason ever to fear it would be attempted.

Do you want to ruin me? is a phrase of capitulation: a kind of dying-speech of a virtue, just going to be turned off.

WANTS

Women of little experience are apt to mistake the urgency of bodily wants, for the violences of a delicate passion; and sometimes are betrayed into this favourable construction by their own exigencies, which do not suffer them to stand examining motives too nicely.

In this case, the appetite is a coarse feeder, that does not stay to pick its bits, but takes the readiest, with a voraciousness that proves more the necessity than the pleasure of the meal. The hunger is all the sauce.

WHO KNOWS *but he may marry me at last?*

A common term, or at least a common thought of girls, who have seen little of the world. It is the usual conclusion of those soliloquies which love, supported by vanity, engages them to make. A man of condition, rich, and struck with the charms of a young person, addresses her, and soon finds the way to her heart. He makes proposals to her, and promises in course. The young creature, full of the prejudices of a virtuous education, tho' poor, rejects them at first. The gallant then sets himself to work to dissipate her fears, and vanquish her scruples. Letters, presents, and especially some female intriguer, who talks all the while of honour, whilst she is labouring to undermine the principles of it, are employed to turn the girl's head, and induce her to accept a lodging well furnished, and a table well kept. The reflexions of the young creature disturb this happiness, she declares she had rather return to her *needlework* than live in infamy. Then the difficulties and inconveniences of marrying, at least *for the present*, are pleaded, and at length believed. The girl returns to her old seducing thought. *Who knows but he may at last marry me?* which had before prevailed, and tranquillizes herself. 'I am adored,' says she to herself; 'I am adorable. So much pains, so many rich presents, are sure proofs of my lover's sincerity: then he is so fine a gentleman: would he deceive me? Why should I despair of my fortune? Why should not I grace a coronet as well as another? Have I less charms than lady such an one, who jumped out of the street into a title and a coach?'

But soon the scene changes, and the illusion vanishes; when my Lord, satisfied with having taken with her the copy of a marriage, proceeds to finish an original one with some lady of fortune or rank equal to his own, or, what is worse, changes one copy for another. Then the *Who Knows* is converted to rants of madness and despair.

THE

CUCKOLD's

CHRONICLE;

BEING

SELECT TRIALS

FOR

| ADULTERY, | IMBECILLITY, |
| INCEST, | RAVISHMENT, &c. |

VOLUME I.

LONDON:

PRINTED FOR H. LEMOIN, BISHOPSGATE CHURCH-YARD.

1793.

THE TRIAL OF THE
CELEBRATED MRS ERRINGTON,
FOR ADULTERY WITH
ARTHUR MURRAY SMITH ESQ.,
CAPTAIN BUCKLEY, CAPTAIN SOUTHBY,
CAPTAIN ROBERTS;
THE REV MR WALKER,
MR TRAYTE, MR CLARKE, AND
MR DANIEL

THE first deposition in this curious trial, is that of Mary
Stevenson, who lived as a servant with Mr and Mrs Errington.
Her evidence amounts to this: that a Captain Smith lived at her
master's house about three months; that her master was in the
profession of the law, and generally left home about eight o'clock
in the morning, and did not return till four or five in the afternoon, or later; that during her master's absence, she has almost
daily seen Captain Smith toying with and kissing her mistress,
and putting his hand in her bosom, and through her pocket-
holes, at which she would seem pleased and happy: at other times
she has seen her mistress sitting on the Captain's knee, with her
arm round his neck, or on his shoulder.

This must have created strange emotions in the bosom of the
spectator, who was then about twenty-three or twenty-four
years of age. She doubtless imagined something was intended
besides picking the lady's pocket, when the Captain put his
hand through her pocket-holes. Her feelings must afterwards
have been greatly heightened; for, from the circumstances that
followed, she must have known that those digitations were a
prelude to a more capital scene.

She then says, that, 'in the absence of her husband, when Captain Smith and her mistress have been together in the parlour,
the little boy has been sent out of the room, and she has frequently, after that, found the door fastened on the inside; and,
her mistress hearing her, would sometimes open the door to

her, and sometimes not, but give her some answer from within; and that, when she has opened the door, she would appear rather embarrassed, her hair being greatly disordered, and her handkerchief and cloaths much rumpled.' She therefore says, that, 'she believes, in her conscience, that the said parties, at such times, had carnal knowledge of each other'.

After mentioning some trifling particulars, such as those of Captain Smith going frequently into her mistress's bed-chamber, and she into the Captain's, and that the beds were afterwards found greatly tumbled; she says, 'she has twice or thrice seen her mistress in the Captain's breeches, coat, and waistcoat; and that, at such times, the Captain and she would help to undress each other'.

Whether Polly Stevenson envied her mistress, we cannot undertake to say; but, it clearly appears, that this toying between the Captain and her mistress, engaged much of her attention, for she often watched them into the hay-loft together, whither they repaired under pretence of finding eggs; and she says, 'her mistress, when she returned, had her cloaths much tumbled, and in great disorder'. At those times, she says, 'she had no doubt upon her mind, that the said parties had the carnal knowledge of each other'.

Mrs Polly also watched the waters of the poor curate of Battersea. Cruel, indeed, that he could not be admitted to give her mistress a little spiritual consolation, but she must put a carnal construction upon his intentions. She says, 'she saw Mr Walker and her mistress come out of the bed-chamber together', and without further evidence of any thing criminal, she runs immediately to the kitchen, and tells her fellow-servants, that she believed 'the parson and her mistress had been in a fit together on the bed'.

How depraved must the mind of Polly Stevenson have been, to form such a supposition! Does she imagine that nothing but carnalities can be practised in a bed-room? Might not he and Mrs Errington, who was one of his parishioners, have been joining in some religious exercises, instead of perpetrating the horrid crime of adultery? Might they not have been conning over the 'lessons of the day', and turning over the sheet of the 'Pilgrim's Progress'? Might he not have pulled out of his pocket 'The Whole Duty of Man', and have pointed out particular

84

interesting practical passages! Was he not, though in a sub-ordinate degree, the shepherd of the parish; and was not she one of his lambs? – But, if a transaction will bear two constructions, Polly seems to delight in giving it the worst. It is possible that, having a strong tendency to fornication herself, she supposes a 'pair of people' cannot go into a 'bed-room' without committing adultery; and actually says, that 'she firmly believes that a criminal connection had passed between them'. She does not indeed mention the gross and indelicate words, 'carnal knowledge'.

She then relates that 'her mistress', being once in a coach with her, put her head out of the window, and asked a smart officer how he did, and he came up to the coach, and the coach stopped, and he opened the door and got in; and Mrs Errington carried him to her husband's house, where he staid tea, and continued alone with her in the parlour some time; and that, from their conversation it appeared, that such officer was an entire stranger to Mrs Errington. That a great intimacy afterwards took place between them, and it appeared that this officer's name was Buckley.

The Captain made his attacks in nearly the same order as Captain Smith, and in particular, regularly besieged the bosom and the pocket-holes. Mary Stephenson observes also, that 'whilst her master was on a journey to Oxford, her mistress staid out all night twice', and seems to conjecture that Captain Buckley was with her.

Jacob Endamaur comes forward as the next witness, and says, 'he was a servant to Mr and Mrs Errington, and has frequently seen Captain Smith and his mistress kissing, toying and romping together, and has seen his mistress sitting upon the Captain's knee, and her hair and cloaths in great disorder'. He makes no criminal charge against the curate, but only says, 'he used now and then to visit and drink tea at the house of his said master, and that he never saw any thing improper pass between him and his mistress'.

He then confirms the evidence given by Mary Stephenson, respecting Captain Buckley, and adds, that 'about two months before he left Mr Errington's service, as he went into the parlour, where Captain Buckley and his mistress were alone together, to throw some coals on the fire, and entering rather suddenly, he saw his mistress sitting in an elbow-chair, and Captain Buckley standing before her; that upon his coming in, Captain Buckley turned immediately away, and appeared to be buttoning up his breeches; and they appeared to be in very great confusion'.

Hence he concludes, that 'they either had been or were prevented by him from being, criminally acquainted together'.

Those, however, who pretend to be in the secret, affirm, that nothing of that kind was then transacting; but the lady was administering something to the Captain, in a particular part, to destroy a species of testaceous insects, which were at that time very troublesome and inconvenient to him. She was acting, it is presumed, the part of 'Lady Bountiful', by endeavouring to destroy such noxious vermin; and yet Jacob Endamaur most uncharitably conjectures, that she was engaged with the Captain in business of a very different nature!

He adds, that 'he has often seen them kissing and fondling each other; and once saw the Captain kissing her naked breast'. He concludes with saying, 'that he does in his conscience believe, that the said parties had frequently had the carnal knowledge of each other'.

Philip Dixon, clerk to Mr Errington, besides confirming some of the particulars already mentioned, deposes, that Captain Buckley, at first, 'would stand in a lane just by the house, as if upon the watch; and, upon those occasions, Mrs Errington would go to him, and bring him home, or stay some time with him, and he has known her stay in the lane with him till eleven o'clock at night. That, at length, the Captain grew more audacious in his behaviour, and would come within about a quarter of an hour after Mr Errington was gone out; and, without asking any question, would run up stairs, whistling or singing, into Mrs Errington's bedchamber, dressing-room, or parlour, wherever she happened to be. That once, in particular, he remembers Captain Buckley and Mrs Errington coming into a room called the library, where the deponent usually sat to write; and, while they were in the room, the Captain went up to her in a very familiar manner, and, as she retired backwards, he followed her until she came with her back against the bookcase; and he then pushed his hand, in a most indecent manner, against her cloaths, between her thighs, and Mrs Errington gently pushed him from her, and they both went out of the room.'

These particulars are so very open and apparent, as to require very little comment or elucidation. Mrs Errington, on their first interview, behaves with great freedom to the Captain; and he in his turn seems to have exactly followed her example. In short, he acted as master of the house, and one would imagine he really thought himself so; but his audacity at last was insupportable; Mr Philip Dixon, therefore, communicated his suspicions, or rather facts, to Mr Errington, and a separation consequently took place between him and his wife, and Mr Dixon believes that Mr Errington has never since cohabited with her.

Another circumstance of her behaviour, mentioned by Mr Dixon, is too material to be omitted. He says, 'Mr Errington's house in Adam-street, was exactly facing the hotel, kept by William Osbourne, in the same street; and that Mrs Errington, when her husband was absent upon business, very frequently went out, and staid for hours together, and often used to return home with various gentlemen, strangers to the deponent, and who appeared but newly acquainted with Mrs Errington.'

There never was a more industrious woman in her line, than our heroine. Idleness she seems to have had an aversion to, and upon all occasions preferred an active life. Her generosity too was unbounded; she did not confine herself to a small circle, and deal out favours with a parsimonious hand, but liberally distributed them to everyone that asked, and frequently even unasked. If the riches of a kingdom depends upon its population (a point in which all our politicians seem to be agreed), Mrs Errington must certainly be a valuable member of society; her whole time is employed in the business of procreation, and she constantly exerts her best endeavours to make new subjects for the state. She has not, indeed, been very successful in her endeavours, therefore she may exclaim, in the language of Addison:

> "'Tis not in mortals to command success,
> But we'll do more, Sempronius, we'll deserve it.'
> CATO.

It is however a just and a general observation, that the ladies who labour too hard in the business of propagation, seldom

87

propagate much. This appears to be precisely the case in the present instance; and, if every woman was as indefatigable in this business as Mrs Errington, the king might 'lack soldiers, and sailors', which would be a heavy loss at this moment.

Luke Carter comes forward next with his testimony. He was also a servant to Mr and Mrs Errington. He says Captain Smith and his mistress used to romp, play, and toy together; and goes upon the same ground as the rest of the witnesses; but says nothing new, except that the Captain used to chuck his mistress under the chin, and gently squeeze her hand. Luke appears to be an arch fellow, and seems to have a particular allusion when he mentions the Captain's 'playing at chuck under the chin'. Probably it was at some considerable distance *under* the chin!

Simon Orchard, aged sixteen years, is the next witness. He was foot-boy to Mr Branston, in Lyme Regis, at a time when Mrs Errington boarded there. He deposes that, 'being one day in his master's parlour upon some errand, Mrs Errington called him to her, and taking a book out of her pocket, shewed him several indecent pictures therein, exhibiting the private parts of both sexes, which she particularly pointed out to him, and told him, such pictures were a representation of the several methods in which gentle-folks and poor folks were connected together'.

Mrs Errington, it must be acknowledged, had always an eye to business, and as poor simple Simon was, at that time, only sixteen years of age, she was apprehensive that he might have been daunted, had she proceeded in a more direct manner. She was determined, however, to have a relish of him, and her mode of angling for him was truly ingenious.

Simon proceeds with his evidence, and says that, 'about two days afterwards, as one Mr Daniel, an attorney's clerk in the town, was passing by on horseback, Mrs Errington tapped against the parlour window, and Mr Daniel immediately alighted, tied up his horse' at the door, and walked in; when Mrs Errington met him at the door, and asked him to take a walk round the garden; and they accordingly walked together in the orchard behind the house, and Simon afterwards saw them sitting upon the grass; but, on their observing him, she came and beat him about the head for watching them, and then returned to Mr Daniel.'

He then relates, that a Captain Roberts, and a Captain Southby, had practised great familiarities with Mrs Errington, and from their having been shut up in rooms together, he supposes they at those times committed adultery.

He next deposes, that 'Mr Trayte, postmaster of Lyme, visited Mrs Errington, and they behaved with great familiarity to each other; that he saw them playing in the orchard together; and, when Mrs Errington ran round the trees, Mr Trayte pursued her till she fell down, and he then caught hold of her, and she said he had hurt her leg, and pulled her petticoats above her knee; and Mr Trayte put his hand upon her knee; that he then assisted her in getting up, and she ran and fell again, and pulled up her petticoats nearly as high as she had done before; that, about half an hour afterwards, they got into the kitchen together, and Mrs Errington went into the store-room and fetched a syringe, which Mr Trayte took from her and filled it with water, and discharged it under her petticoats'.

This appears to have been a very extraordinary kind of amusement for Mr Trayte. After having just had two views above the lady's knee, it is impossible to conceive why he should have recourse to a pewter squirt, and to discharge the contents of it under her petticoats. He may be a tolerable good 'Postmaster', but he must be a wretched 'wh–e–master', not to think of a better expedient to cool the lady's warm premises. Had either of her Captains been then upon duty, they would have acted more 'en militaire'. The post-master of Lyme-Regis stands but a poor chance of obtaining a wife (if he has not already got one) for having worked an improper 'engine', and treated a very 'reverend' looking figure with unbecoming levity.

Soon after this, a very cruel disaster happened to poor Simon, and such a one as fully retaliated for his watching Mr Trayte and Mrs Errington. The poor fellow deposes, that 'the next night, as he was asleep in his bed, he was waked by the bed-cloaths being stripped off him and observed Mrs Errington in her shift only, and Phebe Lush, who then lived fellow servant with him, by his bed-side; and Mrs Errington pulled up his shirt, and caught hold of his private parts, and pulled him out of bed by the same, and said she would pull him down stairs; but he at length got away from her by tearing down the bosom of her shift'.

Alas, poor Simon! If you had not been looked upon as a youth of veracity, I should hardly have credited such a tale; this being the first time, by what I can learn, that Mrs Errington attempted to treat such 'matters' with disrespect, much less with a degree of cruelty. But the most astonishing part of this transaction is, that, after having taken a 'thing in hand', she could ever think of quitting the room till she had finished it. – Perhaps she is not fond of miniatures.

'The next night,' continues master Simon, 'just as he had undressed himself and was going into bed, Mrs Errington came into the room, and made him put on his breeches, and then took him down stairs into her bed-chamber, and placed him under the bedstead of his fellow-servant, Mary Mitchell, which stood even with Mrs Errington's bed, and bade him hide himself till the said Mary Mitchell should come to bed, and was gone to sleep, and that she would then speak to him.'

But when the mistress and maid were undressing to go to bed, the maid heard something breathe hard, and, by the help of the candle, she discovered poor Simon, and sent him to his own bed.

Poor Simon must have thought himself in a very whimsical situation, when placed under Mary Mitchell's bedstead. He was not so entirely an infant, as not to be able to form some imperfect idea of what Mrs Errington meant, when she said she would 'speak to him after Mary Mitchell was gone to sleep'. Simon could not, at that early period, be ignorant of the mode of gestation, though perhaps he had then only a theoretical knowledge of it, and he must have been well convinced, that Mrs Errington intended he should attempt the practical part. It seems evident indeed, that Simon experienced those sensations which such a situation must naturally create, and thought himself amply supplied with materials to act the part of a man, or he would not so readily and quietly have complied with the lady's injunctions of crawling under the bedstead, and to continue in that disagreeable hiding-place, till she ordered him to mount. In the words of the poet, Mrs Errington wanted:

'To teach the young idea how to shoot.'

But it does not appear, from the evidence given, that he was led out of the room in the same manner that he was taken out of bed by Mrs Errington.

The next morning, as master Simon deposes, 'he saw Mrs Errington standing before the fire with her petticoats as high as her knees, in the presence of Phebe Lush, Mary Mitchell, and his master's son, who was then about five years of age, and, seeing some hair lying upon a paper, asked what it was, and the little boy said Mrs Errington had been cutting it off under her petticoats; and then asked Mrs Errington to give him some; when she replied, if she cut off any more, Mr Errington would know it'.

Thus closes the evidence of master Simon: but there appears a deficiency in his deposition; for he does not mention a syllable about the colour of this hair.

Mrs Errington appears, upon all occasions, to consider the propriety of her actions. She did not choose to part with a hair more, lest it should be missed by her husband; but she never thought it necessary to refuse those favours that could not be missed by Mr Errington, though of ten thousand times the value.

Phebe Lush is the next witness in the trial; she corroborates what Simon Orchard had deposed, respecting the mode of Mrs Errington's dragging him out of bed by the middle; she also mentions Mrs Errington's shewing her some indecent pictures and she adds that, one day in the kitchen, she in a very indecent manner took up her petticoats, and, with a pair of scissars, cut off some hair from her private parts, and gave some to Mary Mitchell, and some to this deponent, and bade them keep it for her sake; and, to the best of this deponent's remembrance, Simon Orchard, the foot-boy, came into the kitchen whilst she was about it.

It seems perfectly clear, from what has been already advanced, that the first tuft of hair which was generously bestowed by Mrs Errington to those about her, was all taken from one side of the premises; and the beard appearing afterwards to be rather unequally divided, she gave it a second 'mowing', in order to bring matters into a due proportion and uniformity.

Mary Mitchell next steps forward with her testimony. She was cook to Mr Branston when Mrs Errington boarded at his house. She corroborates the evidence given by several others, and adds, that 'Mr Clarke, one afternoon, amused himself with taking off Mrs Errington's stockings, and putting them on again, frequently kissing her'.

This was a strange kind of penchant of Mr Clarke's! – 'Pulling off her stockings and putting them on again!' It reminds us of Motteaux, who translated Don Quixote. He had a strong propensity to women; but, as he advanced in years, he found it necessary to have recourse to art to give him ability as well as inclination. We never heard, indeed, that he had recourse to the manoeuvre of practising upon legs and stockings, like Mr Clarke; but he had other methods equally extraordinary; and, at length. Nature became so far debilitated, that nothing but hanging by the neck for a few moments, would give him that elasticity necessary for consummation. Extraordinary as it may appear, he frequently submitted to this operation, in order to procure a gratification, which, like Mrs Errington, he considered as the only business worth attending to. At length, however, his life became a forfeit for his imprudence. – He was tuck'd up as usual in a two pair of stairs room, in the presence of three 'filles des joye'; and, just as he was suspended, hearing that some dancing bears were performing in the street, they all ran down to enjoy a sight of the entertainment; and, forgetting, for a while, the situation in which they had left Monsieur Motteux, when they returned, they immediately cut him down, but he was totally incapacitated for business, and also dead! Thus, also, died the musician KOTSWARRA, whose exploits are so brilliantly recorded in a new publication called Modern Propensities.

Mary Mitchell mentions several particulars, which have already been fully related; and, further observes, that, when Mrs Errington shewed the obscene pictures, she would talk in a very immodest manner.

The same witness also says, that 'Captain Southby and Mrs Errington being in a room together, she tried at the door, and found it fastened, or locked within side; that Mrs Errington called from within, and asked her what she wanted; and Mary Mitchell told her the dinner was ready; and she told the deponent it must wait, for she was not ready for it yet; that, in the course of half an hour more, Mrs Errington and Captain Southby came out of the parlour, and the latter went immediately away; that Mrs Errington appeared quite heated, and looked confused, and her hair and cap, and the handkerchief about her neck were in great disorder; that she had no stays on, being in her morning dress, which appeared very much tumbled.' – She adds that, 'she afterwards found the carpet much tumbled, and believes, from her conscience, that the said parties had then the carnal knowledge of each other'.

Mrs Errington, it must be admitted, paid but little attention to her dinners, when matters of more consequence were transacting. We cannot absolutely say how she was engaged while the repast was cooling, but we can give a shrewd conjecture; and Molly Mitchell appears to favour our opinion. The Captain and she, it is supposed, were taking a wet and a relish together; or he might probably be instructing her in some new evolutions, with the modern methods of attack and defence. She is a woman who thirsted after knowledge, and if the Captain had any thing new to communicate, she was sure to pump it out of him. Molly Mitchell supposes the Captain discharged his musket, for, though she did not hear the report, she smelt the powder; and Mrs Errington appeared to have been very much heated in the engagement.

The dinner was now cool, and Mrs Errington, it is presumed, was equally so; for she sat down to table with as much indifference as if she was retiring to bed with her husband. She picked a bit of the wing of a capon, without the least appetite; though, but half an hour before, it is thought, she had a most voracious propensity.

Molly Mitchell relates yet another scene, which has not been deposed to by any of the other witnesses. She says, that she 'once attended Mrs Errington to bathing; and, while she was in the bathing machine, with only her shift and petticoat on, she called to a gentleman, who was a stranger to this deponent, by the name of Love, and desired him to come in, which he did, and staid about a quarter of an hour in the machine with her, and her bosom all the while was quite exposed to his sight'.

The same witness corroborates the clipping scene, and that Mrs Errington gave her and Phebe Lush some hair in a paper, and told them to keep it for her sake, and says, she believes Mrs Errington cut off such hair from her private parts.

Private parts seems to be an improper term here, for what is meant to be understood by it! For, from the immense business which appears to have been transacted there, Molly Mitchell would have expressed herself with more propriety, if she had called them her 'public parts'. But, perhaps, Molly is not censurable in this respect, as the rest of the witnesses make use of the same expression. The term is probably technical, in Doctors Commons, and frequently occurs in their learned and elaborate disquisitions. It is a subject often handled by the professors of ecclesiastical law; and every proctor is so well acquainted with it, that (to use a figurative expression) it is a business that he has at his 'finger ends'.

Towards the conclusion of Mary Mitchell's evidence, she says, with great gravity, 'that she thinks Mrs Errington did not behave in a sober, decent, modest manner'.

Mr Thomas Branston, of Lyme-Regis, gentleman, deposed nothing that has not been already mentioned. But, among other things, he says, that, 'as far as fell under his observation, Mr Errington behaved to his wife with great tenderness and affection, in every respect, as a good husband'.

James Baxter, another witness, says, 'he was watchman and attendant on the officers on guard at the Bank of England, in the riots in June 1780, and still continues in the same situation; that Lieutenant Buckley, of the Coldstream regiment of guards, used occasionally to do duty there; and that Mrs Errington, towards the latter end of the year 1781, frequently visited him when on duty, and laid with him all night in one and the same bed'.

Captain Buckley, it appears by this, had double duty to perform, and he supposed he was as safe as the Bank from discovery; but master James Baxter, who had been engaged by the city to prevent riots, could not endure such riotous proceedings. He thought it an abominable offence, that people who were not free of the city, should come within the centre of its walls, to commit the foul crime of adultery. Had any one of the aldermen or common-council thought proper to amuse himself with a lady on his premises, he would, perhaps, like a good citizen, have winked at it; but for people to bring their harlots from the Westminster end of the town, to defile the more pure city of London, was a matter which his conscience would not permit him to conceal from the community.

Another witness, named Samuel Organ, who is a waiter at Mr Osbourne's hotel, in the Adelphi, says, that 'Mr and Mrs Errington, at one time, lived in a house opposite to his master's; that, at first, from the loose manner of Mrs Errington's behaviour, he concluded she was not married, but a kept woman; that he has frequently seen her standing at her chamber-window, dressed very loosely, and her bosom all exposed; and, from the front window of her house, he has frequently seen her making signs to gentlemen who have happened to be at the said hotel; that her behaviour at the window was in general so very immodest, that his master and mistress often complained of it to gentlemen who came to their house, and hoped they would not take any notice of her.'

Mrs Errington had no very particular attachments, but was equally hospitable to all mankind. If business was but done, she little regarded by whom it was performed; a new morsel now and then, from the Hotel, must have been an excellent repast for her, and she never thought it any indelicacy to communicate her designs, whether by gestures, words, or motions.

Edward Palmer, another waiter at Osbourne's hotel, says, 'he has often seen Mrs Errington half naked at the chamber window, and seen her throw herself into a variety of indecent postures; and has frequently been called by gentlemen, who have been at his master's house, to come and look at her'.

He also deposes that he delivered a letter to her, from a gentleman, which she read, and afterwards desired to see the gentleman, and that such gentleman went to her house accordingly. He adds, that when Mrs Errington was throwing herself into indecent postures, he once saw her naked thighs.

The celebrated heroine of the preceding paper, whose maiden name was H——t C——n, discovered in her early days a violent predilection for gallantry. Her remarkable sprightliness and vivacity, led her on to romping with the boys at the boarding-school, to whom she found means of access, and, notwithstanding all the care of her friends, and the vigilance of her guardian, she had like to have over-leaped all bounds, by taking a trip to Gretna-Green, before she was well entered into her teens.

At the age of fifteen, Miss Harriet set her tender heart on a promising youth; and shewed much emotion and sensibility on occasion of his death, which was by bathing in the Thames.

In her sixteenth year, the most heedless spectator might have run and read the language of her susceptible soul, in her sparkling eyes, comely smiles, and high heaving bosom. The fragrance of spring was not so delightful as her breath; the roses of summer bloomed in her cheeks. She arose to perfection, attracted the eyes of the gay and wanton youths; and grew the envy of her sex. At nineteen, the fair one anticipated the springing pleasures of the distant day, and longed to peep into the page of futurity.

Accordingly, Miss Harriet, accompanied by her maid, visited the gypsies of Norwood, and received from those pretenders to soothsaying, certain dark predictions which highly pleased her fond imagination; beholding a representation of those scenes in which she was to act a capital part.

It is said, that these false augurs presented Miss a spouse, whose air and address but ill accorded with her warm wishes; because he appeared employed chiefly in disputing with the parson about tythes; and engaged in a study rather too dry for a lady of her vigorous and volatile deportment.

As in a mirror, Miss saw the day dawning, wherein her pleasures were to begin. All her future favours were set before her sight, just as they afterwards actually appeared. The Curate, Post-master, Captains, Footman, Butler, Baker and an uncounted croud of fine fellows, passed on in procession, in the manner of the kings in Macbeth. Those who believe in predestination, will easily make an apology for the misconduct of our fair inconstant; for surely a poor weak woman can never be supposed capable of thwarting the decrees of fate itself; and those who cast the greatest weight into the scale of free-will, must reflect on the many temptations which urged her on to deviate from the thorny paths of virtue, and tread the more soft and flowery ones of pleasure.

Miss Harriet, in due time, bestowed her gentle hand on Mr Errington, and made him happy in her charms; in time she produced a pledge of their mutual love; or, to use the language of the law, 'they lived and cohabited together, bed and board, as husband and wife, and consummated their marriage by the procreation of children'. So truly loving were they in their lives, during the first twelve-months, that they might with a great degree of propriety have demanded the flitch of bacon at Dunmow. Happy, they dwelt on the banks of the silver Thames, in the pleasant village of Battersea; and in that Elysium, might have long enjoyed the purest pleasures, without a mixture of alloy, had not an insinuating serpent entered their paradise, and by his cunning, seduced this daughter of Eve, to taste the forbidden fruit, that grew in the 'middle' of the garden.

The first tempter shall be nameless, because he is not blazoned on the Bishop's Book of Adultery; although he was the first who cracked the commandment with our fair but frail spouse. His tongue was more insinuating than oil, and his gnomon of a marvellous projection. His shoulders were broad, his limbs stout as those of Hercules: in fine, his make was masculine throughout, and not a mite of the maccaroni was blended in his athletic frame. The man who charged his back with the gates of Gaza, was not much stronger, when he lay in the lap of Dalilah.

He soon enflamed the heart of the lady, attracted her ear to his tale, and pointed out all the W——s of antiquity, and the Adulteresses of his own day, as examples for the fair one to follow. He gained his point. Mrs Errington yielded, and so pursued the road to pleasure, or rather to disgrace, from which she could never after recede.

THE
TRIAL of WIT,
OR, A NEW
RIDDLE-BOOK

Some of which were never before publifhed.

Compofed for the Benefit of all thofe who
defire to try their WIT, by reading thefe
merry Queftions and Anfwers.

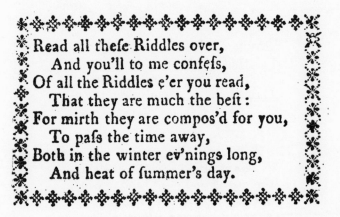

Read all thefe Riddles over,
    And you'll to me confefs,
Of all the Riddles e'er you read,
    That they are much the beft:
For mirth they are compos'd for you,
    To pafs the time away,
Both in the winter ev'nings long,
    And heat of fummer's day.

GLASGOW:
Printed in the year M,DCC,LXXXII.

Pleasantly growing in a bed,
Of complexion white and red,
The fairest lady in the land,
Desires to have me in her hand,
And put me in her hole before,
And wish she had two handfuls more.
And wish she had two handfuls more.
            A Strawberry

A maid in very neat attire
Was occupying by the fire,
She took a thing, and put it to,
It was so slender 'twould not do,
She try'd again, it did not miss,
Ah, quoth she, I am glad of this.
            A Maid threading a Needle

With smock sore rent, and back sore bent,
I playing was by night,
A slipp'ry thing with good intent,
Thrust hard and went in right.
            Kneading dough

Its hairless head is round and knobby,
Its skin is black, strong is its body,
The master and it go hand in hand,
'Tis us'd in secret at command.
            A dark Lanthorn

There is a thing both long and stiff,
And at the end there is a cliff;
Soft moisture from it doth flow,
And makes fair ladies pleasant grow.
            A Pen

100

Although I'm low, yet I'm very fair,
And ladies use me every where,
They kiss me, in their breasts I please,
And 'tis oft said I give them ease;
I'm welcome to her by day and by night,
Although I hurt her when I don't do right.
A Pin

My lady has a thing most rare,
Round about it grows much hair,
She takes delight with it in bed,
And often strokes its hairy head.
A lap-Dog

There is a thing both long and white,
Which pleases ladies in the night;
A moisture comes from its red nose,
The longer it stands the shorter it grows.
A Candle

What's that in which good housewives take delight,
Which, though it has no legs, will stand upright,
'Tis often us'd, both sexes must agree,
Beneath the navel, yet above the knee;
At the end it has a hole; 'tis stiff and strong,
Thick as a maiden's wrist and pretty long:
To a soft place 'tis very oft apply'd,
And makes the thing 'tis us'd to, still more wide;
The women love to wriggle it to and fro,
That what lies under may the wider grow:
By giddy sluts sometimes it is abus'd,
But by good housewife's rubb'd before its us'd,
That it may fitter for their purpose be,
When they to occupy the same are free.
Now tell me merry lasses if you can,
What this must be, that is no part of man?
A Rolling Pin

In the bed it stands, in the bed it lies,
Its lofty neb looks to the skies.
The bigger it is the goodwife loves't the better;
She pluckt it and suckt it, till her eyes did water.
She took it in her hand and said it was good,
Put it in her belly and it stirr'd up her blood.

An Onion

I have a knack above my knee,
And in the middle a hole there be,
Forth came a young man lusty and strong,
And put in a thing two handfuls long.

A Maid had a Sheath, and a young Man
put a Knife into it

Satan's Harvest Home:

OR THE

PRESENT STATE

OF

WHORECRAFT,	PIMPING,
ADULTERY,	SODOMY,
FORNICATION,	And the
PROCURING,	GAME at FLATTS;

(Illuftrated by an Authentick and Entertaining Story)

And other SATANIC WORKS, daily propagated in this good Proteftant Kingdom.

Collected from the Memoirs of an intimate Comrade of the Hon. *Jack S**n**r*; and concern'd with him in many of his Adventures.

To which is added,

The PETIT MAITRE, a POEM,

By a Lady of Diftinction.

LONDON:

Printed for the Editor, and fold at the *Change*, St. *Paul's*, *Fleet Street*, by DOD againft St. *Clement's Church*; LEWIS, *Covent Garden*; *Exeter Change*, at *Charing Crofs*, and in the Court of Requefts; JACKSON, JOLLIFFE, DODSLEY, BRINDLEY, STEIDEL, SHROPSHIRE, CHAPPEL, HILDYARD, at *York*; LEAK, at *Bath*; and at the Snuff Shop in *Cecil Court*, St. *Martin's Lane*, 1749.

THE PRESENT STATE
OF WHORECRAFT

When a Person unacquainted with the *Town*, passes at Night thro' any of our principal Streets, he is apt to wonder, whence that vast Body of *Courtezans*, which stands ready, on small Purchase, to obey the Laws of Nature, and gratify the Lust of every drunken Rake-hell, can take its Rise.

Where the Devil do all these B—hes, come from? being a common Fleet Street Phrase, and in the Mouth of every Stranger; when each revolving Evening sends them up from *White-Chapel* to *Charing Cross* as plenty as Mackrel after Thunder in hot Season.

The Gallants of this Age indeed, are not quite so sturdy as that *Roman Emperor*, who deflower'd ten *Samaritan* Virgins. They destroy, it is true, a great deal of Beauty by only browsing upon the Buds.

Neither is it entirely from a Wantonness of Fancy, or a luxurious Taste of Pleasure, that Men indulge themselves in making this Havock, but chiefly for their own personal Safety. Young Girls are so giddy, thoughtless and unexperienc'd, and withal so fond of the Sport at their first setting out, that they seldom escape a Taint, and a Man is not safe in being constant: nay, some Men are afraid of venturing, even after themselves. By this Means, several likely Women, who might do the Town signal Service, are in a short Time render'd useless: and, by a modest Computation, we are put to the Expence of as many virtuous Women in one Year, as might reasonably serve the Nation six.

What a deplorable Sight is it, to behold Numbers of little Creatures pil'd up in Heaps upon one another, sleeping in the publick Streets, in the most rigorous Seasons, and some of them whose Heads will hardly reach above the Waistband of a Man's Breeches, found to be quick with Child, and become burthensome to the Parish, whose Hospitable Bulks and Dunghils have given them Refuge? I have often thought, that the removing these Lay-Stalls of Leachery from the Doors of a great Protestant City, might not be a Work altogether unworthy of our reforming Scavengers.

We often read, indeed, of the mighty Atchievements of a certain *Kn—t*, and the Excursions of Midnight *Constables*; their encount'ring of Dragons in Gin-shops, storming enchanted Night-Cellars, and leading Ladies into Captivity. All which are related with wonderful Exactness in the publick News-Papers. But meet these People when you will, you will seldom find in their Custody above a *Flat-Cap* or a *Cinder-Wench*, who, because their Rags won't pawn for a Dozen of Beer, are made Examples of. She that has the Prudence to whore with Half a Crown in her Pocket, is as sure of a Protection, as a cheating *Director*, and may sin on without any Danger. While the poor needy *Wag-Tail* must be cautious how she kisses, lest she be carried to *Bridewel*, where, instead of being reclaim'd, she is harden'd by her indelible Shame in her miserable State of Wickedness. The only good they have done, is to put an Impost upon Whoring, and made themselves Collectors of the Duty; for which Reason, the Price of Venery is greatly enhanc'd, and that within a few Years, which makes it the more practised; for the Cheapness of a Commodity always throws it out of Fashion, and Things easily purchas'd are seldom minded. It is a right Observation, that Restraint does but whet the Passions, instead of curing them, as we find in the Case of most married Men, who like *Sampson's* Foxes, only do more Mischief for having their Tails tied.

The late Colonel *Chart—s* was indeed of Opinion, that when we caught a fine *Sempstress* or *Mantua-Maker*, in the publick Streets after Nine at Night, whether *Banbox'd* or *Bundl'd*, it might still be lawful to charge her in Custody of the first Hackney Coach, and convey her to the next Bagnio, as a proper and rightful Chattel of the Publick's; but how far that Gentleman's Sentiments will be supported by our Statutes, I must leave to the Determination of the Learned.

The Town being over-stock'd with Harlots, is entirely owing to those Numbers of *Women-Servants*, incessantly pouring into it from all Corners of the Universe, and those Debaucheries practis'd upon 'em in almost all the Families that entertain them: *Masters*, *Footmen*, *Journeymen*, *Lodgers*, *Apprentices*, &c are for ever attempting to corrupt; and few young Creatures now-a-days are endow'd with a Stock of Virtue sufficient to hold out against all their Attacks; so that a poor Wench, who serves for four or five Pounds a Year Wages, shall be liable to go through

as much *Drudgery*, as a Livery-Horse, that's lett out to a City Prentice *for a Sunday's* Airing.

I am told, it is the Custom throughout the *West* of *England*, that when a young Girl is taking leave of her Friends and Relations to come for *London* and seek her Fortune, while some of them are wishing her *Grace*, and others *a good Place*, and the Carrier is hoisting her up into his Waggon, to give her a swinging Thump on the Br—ch, saying,

> *Now Hussey a Month's Wages or a Month's Warning,*
> *And to Bed to your Master every Morning.*

After they have been a little while in Town, and had some Feather-Bed Instruction, and are out of Place, and having nothing to support them, they then prostitute their Bodies. Many of them are as restless as a *new Equipage*, running from Place to Place, from Bawdy-House to Service, and from Service to Bawdy-House again; for, if the Matron uses them ill, away they trip to Service, and if their Mistress but gives them a wry Word, whip they are as ready to be gone, *as a reliev'd Guard*, or *a discharg'd Jury*: so that in Effect, they neither make good Whores, good Wives, or good Servants, and this is one of the chief Reasons why our Streets swarm with Strumpets.

What is more common, than to find the Daughters of mean Tradesmen, basking in their Beds at Ten o'Clock in a Summer's Morning, and when call'd on to *rise*, must have good Assurances of the *Tea-Kettle's* being up before them, e'er they'll vouchsafe to begin to rub their Eyes and Posteriors, and put themselves in a way of slipping on a loose Petticoat, Night-Gown and Slippers; by which, and the Addition of a foul Handkerchief, a Play-book, and Snuff-Box, Miss is compleatly equipt for the Tea Table.

Thus their silly fond Parents, who perhaps are scarce able to give fifty Pounds Portion with them, indulge them from their Infancy in every slothful Habit. Any idle Complaint suffices, to keep a Child a Week from Work or from School. I have seen my Landlady's Daughters romping about the Street all the Forenoon: *Children*, said I, *why are not you gone to School? O Sir, we ben't well.*

Impudence and Idleness soon gain the Ascendancy over them, and then it is, that a Wench of fourteen, fancies herself as fit for

Man, and ripe for Joy, as a Woman of five and twenty: and then also, we behold a strange Paradox; that a Girl, who cou'd never be taught to the Use of her *Needle*, becomes on a sudden a wonderful Proficient in the Art of *stitching*.

I have frequently smil'd, to see a debauch'd *Veteran*, Ogling a fine Woman at Church, and taking a View of the Fortifications. Some Women are naturally more chaste, or rather, to speak properly, less amorous than others, and at the same Time have very strict Notions of Honour. Such Women are almost impregnable, and may be compar'd to Towns strongly fortified both by Art and Nature, which, without Treachery, are safe from any Attacks, and must be reduc'd by long and regular Sieges, such as few Men have the Patience and Resolution to go thro' with: unless their Charms are very great indeed, sufficient to provoke Men to be at any tolerable Pains and Cost, and then their Chastity can never hold out long, but must infallibly surrender.

Others, who have a very moderate share of Honour, join'd to a very amorous Constitution, their Virtue is intirely Defenceless; and as soon as a Man has remov'd that little timorous Coyness, which is natural to young Women in their first Attempts, he may proceed with Confidence, and conclude the Breach to be practicable; for, whatever Resistance he meets with afterwards, will only enhance the Pleasure of Conquest. Most Women, indeed, let them be ever so fully resolved to comply, make as great a shew of Resistance as they can conveniently counterfeit; and this the Sex would palm upon the World for a kind of innate Modesty.

Not to mention the actual Pleasure a Woman receives in struggling, it is a Justification of her, in the Eye of the Man, and a kind of *Salvo* to her Honour and Conscience, that she never did fully comply, but was in a Manner forc'd into it. This is the plain Reason, why most Women refuse to *surrender* upon Treaty, and why they delight so much in being *storm'd*.

Hudibras has ludicrously plac'd the Seat of Male Honour in the Posteriors, whereby it is secur'd from any Attack in Front; but Female Honour, notwithstanding the apparent Safety of the Situation, like a Debtor's House upon the Verge of two Counties, is liable to be attack'd both Ways, *à Parte ante, & à Parte post*.

In short, these Things rightly consider'd, it can no longer be wonder'd at that Men shew so little Inclinations to marry, when they see a *Maidenhead's* as easy to be obtain'd as a *Peace-Warrant*, and the one granted upon a *single Oath*, as well as the other.

Passing by a Bagnio one *Sunday* Morning, I was not a little surpriz'd, to hear a fine personable Man, drest in a rich Suit of lac'd Cloaths, and taking Chair, give Orders to be set down at the Parish-Church; while the Gentlewoman of the House, who waited on him to the Door, charg'd the Chairmen to proceed with the utmost Expedition, because it was a Case of Necessity, the Gentleman being oblig'd to be timely there, to *Qualify* for a considerable *Post* in the Army.

There are some rich generous Sinners, who in the Winter of their Leachery, only keep a Wench for the Pleasure of now and then obliging a Bottle Companion. A *Madam* once shew'd me a *Draught* that her *Friend*, as she affected to call him, had just made upon her; and having obtain'd a Copy, I thought I could do no less than oblige my courteous Readers with it.

August 23, 1748.

Dear MOLLY,

On Sight hereof permit the Bearer, to immediately enter a Pair *of* Holland *Sheets with you; let him have Ingress, Egress and Regress to your person, in such Manner as to him shall meet, for the Space of twenty-four Hours, and no longer, and place it to the Account of*

	Your kind and
King's-Arms *Tavern*,	Constant Keeper,
Four in the Afternoon	EDMUND EASY.

P.S. *Child go through all your Exercises and Evolutions, as well for your own as my Credit.*

But what amazes and fills all Mankind with Wonder and Surprize, is a *new Vice* started upon us, introduced and boldly led up by Women of the first Figure and Fortune as well as Fashion, worthy the Imitation of the whole Sex. These, *vice versa*, have inverted the Order of Things, turn'd the Tables upon the Men, and very fairly begun openly to *Keep their Fellows*: for Ladies during the Bands of Wedlock, as well as in a State of Widowhood, to call in private *Aid, Assistance* and *Comfort*, is an Immunity they've enjoy'd time immemorial:

but for the *Fair*, and such as even profess Spinsterhood, to keep Men in private Lodgings, and visit them publickly in their Equipages, are Privileges unknown to our Ancestors.

I don't know indeed how far the *Sex* may value themselves upon this notable Discovery, which perhaps they may fancy to be a just Method of Reprisal; but all sober considering People will look upon the Thing, as it certainly is, a most enormous Sin to lay Snares for the Unwary, and be the Means of ruining both Souls and Bodies of so many innocent young Gentlemen: to which, however, I hope, the Wisdom of the Nation will put a speedy and effectual Stop, otherwise it will be no difficult Matter to forsee what infinite Numbers of Men must inevitably be made miserable.

These Harlots at first play at a high Game; nothing will serve some of them, less than a Settlement of *two or three Hundred Pounds* per *Annum, a Coach, fine Lodgings suitable for a Whore of Rank,* and upon these Considerations, she'll be faithful to you, or at least she'll promise you she will: but this is only a Promise *de Facto* neither; so long as your Estate lasts, and you can maintain her in her Extravagance and Grandeur; but when that fails, so does the Obligation too; she has the grand political Reasons ready, as well as the best Statesmen of 'em all, and commonly makes the same Use of 'em.

She can pray, cant, shed a few Crocodile Tears, or rather than fail, sham a Fit, as a Token of the Passion and Tenderness she has for you; but then your Back's no sooner turn'd, but she tells her *Stallion* you're a nasty, sickly, feeble Fellow, and that as soon as she has persuaded you out of the Settlement, and the new Furniture, she'll first affront you and then leave you.

If he finds you are a Cully indeed, and will be often impos'd upon by her, then she has a Thousand little wheedling Tricks and Artifices to decoy, and which she practises, even in the tender *Minute*; sometimes she's *breeding* forsooth, and then sure you cannot be so barbarous to *your own Flesh and Blood*, but you will take some Care of the *young One*; besides, she wants Night-Gowns, and Damask for Clouts, and a Thousand other Necessaries for a lying-in Woman.

There's my Lord *A—s*, and Sir *John B—s*, and Colonel *D—s* Misses, lay-in as much State the other Day, as the best Lady in the Kingdom; nay, Mr *F—*, who is but an ordinary

Citizen, presented his Concubine with a Bed and the Furniture of a Room, that cost him above *two Hundred and fifty Pounds;* and what has she, I wonder, done, that she should not deserve as much as the best of them? Why, sure's she's as handsome, and as young, and as capable of her Duty, as any of them, and do you think she'll be put off with your nasty shabby forty or fifty Guineas? No, truly, she rather thinks, that as Cases stand between you and her, you ought to cut off the Entail of your Estate, and settle a good Part of it upon her for her Life, and then let the Child heir it afterwards. And perhaps all this too may be Whore-craft and Pretences, and so she must be forced (to bring herself off) to sham a Miscarriage, and that your Cruelty and hard-heartedness in not settling your Estate upon her, and answering her Demands, has been the Cause of it, and will at last force her to make away with herself. Well, but if you lov'd her as well as she loves you, you could not be so barbarous to deny her any Thing.

Besides, she has been no chargeable Mistress to you neither; she has been your Drudge for at least these seven Months, and han't cost you fifteen Hundred Pound in the whole. If you had liv'd with some she knows in the Town so long (but she is an easy Fool), 'twould have stood you in not a Penny less than three Thousand.

Their Tricks and Devices are numberless, and not to be parallel'd by any Thing but their Ingratitude and Inhumanity; there indeed they exceed themselves; nothing in Nature being so perfectly brutish and cruel as one of these kind of Creatures. The very Moment you stop your Hand, they grow rude and insolent; and when they find they have entirely done your Business, and turn'd you a grazing, who so ready as that very *Syren* that has spent your Estate, to laugh at, revile and scorn you; and you are not less her Buffoon now, than you were formerly her Property.

To have done with her: a JILT is a *Procurer, Bawd* and *Whore*, compounded together. A Vermin so ravenous and malicious, and withal so subtle and designing, so formally chaste and hypocritically virtuous, and yet so scandalously common and impudently lewd, so proud, and yet so mercenary, and above all, so insolently ill natur'd, that in the short Character of a *Jilt*, are comprehended all the Vices, Follies and Impertinences of the whole Sex.

And lastly, for their Art of *trapping*, this is a Mystery that they commonly manage, either by the Assistance of *a pregnant Whore*, or by the Help of some Letters or Papers that they pick out of your Pockets, that gives them an Inlet into your Affairs. The first is carried on by *Procurers*, *Bawds* and *Jilts*, and the latter by *Sharpers*, *Setters* and *Bullies*: if they are once so fortunate to get a big-belly'd Whore into their Confederacy, then they carry her about in a kind of Triumph among all her *Cullies* and *Novices*; every one under the Notion of being the true Father, must subscribe an individual Maintenance for the *Strumpet* and the *Brat*; or a Warrant must be got immediately, or the Overseers of the Parish call'd in to their Assistance to force you to it. 'Tis no matter to contest it, for if you do, they'll force the Woman to swear it upon you, and then your Reputation's lost, and withal you have the Charge of a *Whore* and a *Bastard* entail'd upon you *ad infinitum*.

Let a sober Person take a gentle Walk through the ancient *Hundreds* of *Drury*, where ev'ry half a dozen Steps he meets with some odd Figure or another, that looks as if the *Devil* had robb'd them of all their *natural Beauty*, which being in our Maker's Image, we derive from our Creator, and had infus'd his own infernal Spirit into their corrupt Carcasses; for nothing can be read but *Devilism* in every Feature; *Theft*, *Whoredom*, *Homicide* and *Blasphemy*, peep out of the very Windows of their Souls; *Lying*, *Perjury*, *Fraud*, *Impudence* and *Misery*, the only Graces of their *Countenance*.

One with *slip Shoes*, without *Stockings*, and a *dirty Smock*, visible thro' a torn Petticoat, stepping out of a *Pawn-Broker's Shop*, yet with her Head dress'd up to as much Advantage, as if the Members of her Body were sacrific'd to all Wickedness to keep her ill-lock'd Face in a little Finery. Another, taken from the *Shoe-stool* or *Oyster-tub*, and put into *Whores Allurements*, she makes indeed a more cleanly Appearance, but becomes her Ornaments as a *Welch-Ale-Wife* doth a *Velvet Manteel*, or a *Sow* a *Hunting Saddle*. A third, at the Heels of a Porter hurrying to a Tavern, to sell Half a Crown's Worth of Fornication to a drunken Letcher.

Turn your Eyes up to the Chambers of Wantonness, and you behold the most shameful Scenes of Lewdness in the Windows even at Noonday, some in the very Act of Vitiation, visible to all the opposite Neighbours. Others dabbing their *Shifts*, *Aprons* and *Headcloths*, and exposing themselves just naked to the Passers by. A Gang of *Bailiffs*, *Butchers* and *Highwaymen* are drinking, and damning at an Ale-house Door, then every now and then out bolts a Fellow, and whips nimbly a-cross the Way, being equally fearful both of *Bailiff* and *Constable*, looking as if the Dread of the *Gallows* had drawn its Picture in his Countenance. Here and there a dirty shabby looking *Quack*, going from House to House to visit his rotten Patients, as publickly and openly as a Collector of the King's Tax; and as often call'd to from the Windows of the first to the third Story, to know how such an one goes on in her Salivation.

My Dear, will you give me a Glass of Wine; take me under your Cloak, my Soul, and how does your precious —— do? You hear at the Corner of every Court, Lane and Avenue, the Quarrels and Outcries of Harlots recriminating upon one another, Soldiers and Bullies intermixing, the most execrable Oaths are heard, such as are seldom exceeded, but at a *Stop* of *Carts* and *Coaches* in a Winter's Evening. By and by a Brandy-Shop is going to be demolish'd, because the Master refuses to bail some Whore that's just arrested, and a Coach waiting at the Door of her Lodgings to carry her to the Officer's House, unless he does the kind Office. A Riot breaks out in another Place, a Bawd's Goods are seized on for Rent; a new Tumult ensues, a Whore's Maid in crossing the Croud, has a Misfortune to break a Bottle of red Port, with a Couple of Pipes, that she is carrying to her Mistress's Chamber, the Mob give a Shout, the Girl is beat out of Doors with her Head bloody, all the Chandler-Women and Gin People are assembled, with an *Irish* Sollicitor at their Head about the Door, with an Outcry for *Justice*; poor *Peggy's* Rashness is blamed by some, and justified by others; in an Instant half a dozen Suits of Head Cloths are torn in Pieces, and several black Eyes and bloody Noses exhibited; *Warrants, binding over*, and *Actions*, are the Subjects of all Conversation in *Coulson's-Court, Bridges-Street*, &c. A Cry of Murder is heard about twenty Yards farther, a *Mother* or *Father* being under the bastinading of a dutiful *Son* or *Daughter*. *Pimps* and *Pensioners* to the *Hundred*, you see skulking from Bawdy-House to Bawdy-House incessantly. In short, I cannot but fancy them a Colony of *Hell-Cats*, planted here by the Devil, as a Mischief to Mankind; they admit of no Comparison on this side Hell's Dominions, all this Part, quite up to *N—wtn—rs Lane, Park—er's Lane, St Th—mas's-street* (some few honest Shop-keepers excepted), is a Corporation of *Whores, Coiners, Highwaymen, Gamesters, Pick-pockets,* and *House-breakers,* who like *Bats and Owls* skulk in obscure Holes and *Geneva* shops by Day-Light, but wander in the Night in search of Opportunities wherein to exercise their Villany.

An Inhabitant of this antient *Sodom,* has inform'd me, that the eight Sessions of Oyer and Terminer, generally holden every Year at the *Old Bailey,* together with the Act for the Transportation of Felons, had considerably lower'd the Rents in this Precinct, within a few Years, and greatly thinn'd the People, insomuch, that the half of some Streets and Allies were entirely depopulated; but, that the greatest Shock the Place ever receiv'd, was from the *Develian* Persecution, which had driven great Numbers of Families out of their *Free-holds,* and scatter'd them all over the City and Suburbs, whereby the Trade and Business was chiefly remov'd to other Places, viz. the *Fourscores* of *Fleet-street* and *Shoe-Lane,* the *Fifties* of *Dukes-place* and the *Minories,* and the *Course* of *Charing-cross,* which last was now render'd in as flourishing a Condition, as in the Reign of King *Charles* the IId, there being little else but Concubines in all the Lodgings, and nothing but *lascivious Looks* seen in the Chamber-Windows, from one End of the *Verge* to the other: nor are very few of these the *Propriety* of *one Man,* but ordain'd for the *Comfort* and *Refreshment* of *Multitudes,* devoting themselves to the Service of ALL the loving Subjects of *Great-Britain*; such gay Volunteers give a young Fellow an handsome Prospect of the Town, leading him thro' all the *inchanting* Mazes, and even surfeit him with *Delight,* so that by the Time he is come out of their Hands, he is become very tame, and prepar'd for the dull Solemnity of *Marriage.*

There liv'd till about a Year ago, an elderly Woman, near *King-street, Westminster,* who was every Day very needful in the World, yet every Day did a World of Mischief; who kept a House of free Hospitality, but made Folks pay vastly dear for what they had. But her Customers paid the greatest Price with the greatest Pleasure; for this celebrated Sinner dealt not in Trifles, such as *Wines* and *Ragousts,* but in Nervous Aches and Rottenness of Bones; she had always a Bible in her Hand at home, and always a to-be-ruin'd Damsel abroad; each Morning she took her Rounds to all the Inns, to see what Youth and Beauty the *Country* had sent to *London* to make their Fortunes; and when she found a Rural pretty Lass step out of a Waggon, she drew her by her smooth Language to a private Box within, where, after telling the harmless Girl, *'twas pity such well-shap'd Limbs should twirl a Mop; such red and white Cheeks should be sullied with Cinders and Charcoal; such a ready Wit be subjected to the unreasonable Clamours of a bawling Mistress*: this antiquated *she Captain* of *Satan's* Regiment, would offer the poor innocent Creature an Apartment, and all Accommodations in her House *gratis*, till she saw if she should like the Town, *for 'twas but a sad wicked Place, full of Temptations for young Girls, but the Almighty would deliver his good Children*. At other Times, she would go to the *Hospitals* and *Bridewel*, and pick out all the well-limb'd Creatures, these she'd trick up with Patch and Paint, and lett out at extravagant Prices: always calling them young *Milliners* or *Parsons* Daughters. Indeed some shabby abandon'd Fellows, who us'd (for Mercenary Ends) to smile at the old Matron herself, and chuck her under her wicked Chin, she'd relieve with a Supper, and sometimes afford them an After-Course, *viz.* some of her young Wares who appear'd to her the least Marketable. But such miserable Chaps as these (who tho' abandon'd by the World, could not abandon their Vices), she did not much care for; observing, perhaps, with others, that the worse their Circumstances, the greater their Assurance.

If you meet with any of our Trading Madams, and ask them *who debauch'd her*, it is ten to one, but her Answer will be *Jack* ——. I have heard of above 500 unfortunate Women, who have laid their *Virginities* at the Door of this *young Gentleman*. At the latter End of Queen *Anne's* Reign, a certain Viscount had the *Reputation* of *deflowering* far and near; the Elegance of whose Taste was esteem'd such, that it was rather a Recommendation, than Impediment to the Woman's *Marriage*, or her future *keeping*, if she had but once pass'd the *Hand* and *Seal* of Mr *Secret—ry*. A merry but true Story, is related on that Occasion, *viz.* a Courtezan being met in the *Mall* by a Gentleman, he ask'd *whether she had heard the News — Pray what is it? — Why, your old Friend* H—ry St J—hn, *is made* S—c—y *of* St—e. *What may that be worth*, says the Lady — *Perhaps about* 10000*l. a*

Year. —*By G—d I'm glad to hear it with all my Soul, for the Wh—res will get every Penny of it.*

In the *City*, every undone Woman lays her Ruin, *to a Gentleman of the Temple*, but whether these Things are justly laid to their Charge, or whether it is only the Ambition of the *Jilt*, to have you think she sacrific'd her Virginity to the Use of so worthy a Society, I will not presume to determine; tho' I confess, I think it reasonable to believe, that our forward Ladies are more apt to dedicate their Honours to the *Inns of Court* than elsewhere, for three Reasons: *first*, as they are the Flower of our Gentry. *Secondly*, as the Greatness of their Number affords Variety of Choice. And, *thirdly*, as they have the best Conveniencies for consummating Debauchery, without the Dread or Danger of Detection.

The greatest Evil that attends this Vice, or could befal Mankind, is the Propagation of that infectious Disease call'd the *French Pox*, which in two Centuries, has made such incredible Havock all over *Europe*. In these Kingdoms, it so seldom fails to attend Whoring, now-a-days mistaken for Gallantry and Politeness, that a hale robust Constitution is esteem'd a Mark of Ungentility and Ill-breeding, and a healthy young Fellow is look'd upon with the same View, as if he had spent his Life in a Cottage. Our Gentlemen of the Army, whose unsettled Way of Life makes it inconvenient for them to marry, are hereby very much weaken'd and enervated, and render'd unfit to undergo such Hardships, as are necessary for defending and supporting the Honour of their Country; a remarkable Instance whereof happen'd the other Day near *Knightsbridge*, where two Subalterns, *viz. a Lieutenant* with his Half-pike, and an *Ensign* with his Colours, were unhappily by a sudden Gust of Wind blown into a Ditch in their March to *Kensington*: and our Gentry in general, seem to distinguish themselves by an ill state of Health; in all Probability, the Effect of this pernicious Distemper. Nothing being more common, than to hear People of Quality complain of *rude vulgar Health*, and curse their *Porterly Constitutions*. Men give it to their Wives, Women to their Husbands, or perhaps their Children; they to their Nurses, and the Nurses again to other Children; so that no Age, Sex or Condition, can be entirely free from the Infection.

Another ill Effect, is, its making People profuse, and tempting

them to live beyond what their Circumstances will admit of; for if once Men suffer their Minds to be led astray by this unruly Passion, no worldly Consideration whatsoever, will be able to stop it; and Wenching, as it is very expensive in itself, without the ordinary Charges of *Physick* or *Children*, often leads Men into a Thousand other Vices to support its Extravagance: besides, after the Mind has once got this extravagant Turn, there naturally follows a Neglect and Contempt of Business, and Whoring of itself disposes the Mind to such a sort of Indolence, as is quite inconsistent with Industry, the main Support of any, especially of a Trading Nation.

ECLIPSE RACES,

(Addreſſed to the LADIES:)

BEING AN

IMPARTIAL ACCOUNT

OF THE

CELESTIAL COURSERS and their RIDERS,

Starting togéther, *April* 1, 1764,

FOR THE

ECLIPSE-PLATE-PRIZE.

Their *Diſtinctions* and *Atchievements.*

Thoſe who were *Competitors, diſtanced, thrown out,* or met with *Accidents,* in the contending ENTERPRIZE.

Who won the PRIZE.

Popular Fears and Apprehenſions, with *ſuitable* REMARKS.

And the true APPEARANCE of the RACES repreſented.

Some CUSTOMS, in our public OBSERVATORIES and *Mathematical* SCHOOLS, referred to the *Conſideration, Power,* and *Juſtice,* of the diſcerning LADIES.

The *Yorkſhire* SYPHON-MAKERS and PHILOSOPHERS : A *Satyr.* INVITATION to *Epſom Races* : A *Song.* TIT-UP : Another *Song.*

O 'twas a gallant *Steed* I rode ! --- train'd up
To *War !* --- Had I known Fear he would have *tham'd* me !
He curl'd his *Creſt,* and proudly paw'd the Ground,
And from his *vocal Noſtrils* neigh'd ſuch Fire !
To mount him ſeem'd the Tranſport of a *Throne !*

Shakeſpear's King *John.*

By PHILO-PEGASUS, a Lover of *Truth.*

LONDON:

Printed for the AUTHOR ; and ſold by J. WHISTON and B. WHITE, W. SANDBY, Bookſellers, and B. COLE, Mathematical-Inſtrument-Maker, *Fleet-ſtreet* ; and ſeveral other Bookſellers and Mathematical-Inſtrument-Makers. MDCCLXIV.

[Price One Shilling.]

TIT-UP

A SONG BY PHILO-PHILLIS,
A LOVER OF THE TURF

I

The Man how silly,
To think he's able
To back a Filly,
When old and feeble,
Sighing, trying,
Striving, Mounting,
Scarce, after all, to his *Saddle* can rise!
But, when upon her,
Head strong he's got,
Now for his *Honour,*
She very *hot;*
Suddenly she plunges,
Capers and lunges,
Off he is flung, and *away Philly flies!*

II

But let the clever
Jolly young Rider,
While you live ever,
Mount her, he'll guide her;
Freaking, Squeaking,
Neighing, playing,
Sweetly she'll move to his Pleasure and Ease;
Walk, Trot, and Gallop,
And quite in Hand,
Warm with her *Glee* up,
At your Command,
Freely she'll set up,
Tit-up, a Tit-up,
Tit-up, a Tit-up, as long as you please.

VENUS UNMASKED:

OR, AN

INQUIRY

INTO THE

NATURE AND ORIGIN

OF THE

PASSION OF LOVE.

Interfperfed with

Curious and Entertaining Accounts

OF SEVERAL

MODERN AMOURS.

IN TWO VOLUMES.
VOL. I.

O happy State ! where Souls each other draw,
Where Love is Liberty, and Nature, Law :
All then is full, poffeffing and poffefs'd,
No craving Void left aching in the Breaft :
Ev'n Thought meets Thought ere from the Lips it part,
And each warm Wifh fprings mutual from the Heart.

Pope's Epift. from Eloifa to Abelard.

LONDON:
Printed for the AUTHOR.
And Sold by M. THRUSH, at the King's-Arms
in Salifbury-Court, Fleet-Street. 1759.

THE NATURE AND ORIGIN OF LOVE

An Account of several Experiments made by
a Lady who had adopted the System of Sympathy

A Lady of Quality, at *Florence*, conceived so high an Idea of the System of Sympathy, when it was first explained to her, that she became one of its warmest Votaries, and formed a Resolution to spare no Pains to establish its Credit.

In this Disposition she reflected, that all sound Philosophy is founded upon Experiment; and that she might be at Liberty to try such Experiments as she thought requisite, she had Recourse to a Stratagem.

She drest herself in Man's Clothes; and, attended only by her Woman in the same Disguise, made a Tour to *France*. The Waiting-woman had been initiated into the Mysteries of Sympathy by her Mistress, and was as well disposed as she to confirm it by Experiment. Here it may not be improper to give an Idea of the Person of her who had the Courage to undertake such an Enterprize, and the laudable Constancy to go through with it.

Her Shape was faultless, and had nothing in it that could discover her Sex, except that it was extremely delicate and slender. Her Hair was of the deepest black, as were also her Eyes, which had an uncommon Lustre and Vivacity. Her other Features were perfectly agreeable; and her Air had an engaging Assurance which inspired every Beholder with Pleasure. But to return to our History.

She set out in this Manner, assuming the Character of an *Italian* Marquis upon his Travels. No Opportunity of making any Experiment offered till her Arrival at *Lyons*, where she had the Fortune to meet a *French* Officer, who was upon his Way to *Marseilles*. The Officer saluted our Adventurer with that easy Politeness natural to Men of his Profession, and, after some Conversation not much worth relating, they sat down to Supper, and were neither displeased at seeing that there was no body else at Table. The Officer, who had an excellent Appetite when he came in, was now become unable to eat. His Attention was entirely engaged by the supposed Stranger, whose Presence produced an Effect upon him that he was puzzled to account for. This she observed with secret Pleasure; and whilst his Eyes, which swam with Joy, were fixed on hers, hers were equally dissolved in Bliss, and rolled in that precious Fluid, in which the Loves and Graces seemed to sport.

The young Officer was no great Philosopher; and, consequently, not well enough acquainted with the various Operations of the sympathetick Matter, to distinguish the Sex of the Person he was in Company with, by the Manner in which it acted upon him. However, without perceiving it himself, he behaved to her all the Time they were at Table as a Lover does to his Mistress.

They passed a considerable Time in this Manner, till the supposed Marquis perceiving it grew late, made an Offer to retire; but the Officer, not willing to be so soon deprived of the company of a Person for whom he had conceived so strong an Affection, offered to share his Bed with the unknown Object of his Flame. The Proposition was accepted; and our Heroine, who by the Dint of Philosophy had surmounted the Timidity of her Sex, undressed with Assurance.

Our young Officer, who took off his Cloaths at the same Time, still kept his Eyes fixed on the Marquis, and, at last discovered with Wonder and Delight, something that set him all in a Flame. This was no other than* * * *

Fired with the Sight, he seized the Object of his Passion in his Arms, and carried her to the Bed; she did not vainly attempt to resist one so much stronger than herself, but directing her Eyes downwards, as he had before don his, perceived* * * *

And now let us suppose our Travellers in Bed; how they past the Night is left to the Reader's Imagination. It is reasonable to suppose that it was past

In Extasies too fierce to last for ever.

Fair Penitent

At length the Morning came; but our young Officer was so far from rising with cold Indifference from the luscious Banquet, that it was with the utmost Regret that he took Leave of our fair Adventurer, to join his Regiment, which was upon its March to the Garrison of *Marseilles*. Our Heroine continued her Course of experimental Philosophy; and, in the Prosecution of it, many similar Adventures befel her; but as there must be a

Sameness in Narratives of this Kind, I shall suppress the rest, hoping that what has been said may be sufficient to enable the Reader to form a Judgement of the Remainder.

I shall only add that *Paris*, which has been always more famous for its Gallantries than its Universities, afforded her the most Opportunities of Experiment; and that she added more to her Stock of natural Knowledge by residing there a few Months, than she could have done any where else in as many Years. If the Mistress was successful amongst Persons of Condition, the Maid, who passed for her Valet, was no less so amongst Waiters, Lacquies, and Barbers Boys.

An Account of an extraordinary Cure effected by the Operation of the Sympathetick Matter

A wealthy Merchant of this City, whose Name and Place of Abode I omit for obvious Reasons, had a Daughter of uncommon Beauty. She was of an advantageous Stature, but not too tall neither; her Hair was of a dark brown, her Complexion inclined to the pale, though it did not want Freshness. Her Eyes, which were neither black nor grey, contained more Sweetness than Fire. Her Person was in every Respect graceful, and her Hand and Arm of such peculiar Beauty, that a Painter might have copied them in a Portrait of white-armed *Juno*; and such a Portrait, well executed, would not fail to come up to the Idea of *Homer*. I shall not omit a certain Part which should never be forgotten in these descriptions. Below her ivory Neck, the delighted Spectator discovered a Cliff, which gradually led his ravished Eye to the Contemplation of two snowy Globes, which, though not of the first Magnitude, seemed to court the hand and sue to be prest, as an ingenious Author has happily expressed it.

Such was the hapless Fair One, who, by an avaricious Father, was destined to the nauseous Embraces of a Person labouring under Age and Infirmities; to which he added the additional Horrors of Deformity.

How the young Lady could be prevailed on to accept of such a Husband, may appear extraordinary; and tho' we could give some Account of the Measures taken for that Purpose, yet, as such a Narrative must appear dry and uninteresting, we shall

124

suppose this ill-matched Pair already married, and apply to the Lady those satyrical Lines of the Poet, which seem so apposite on the present Occasion:

> Since thou wouldst needs, bewitch'd by some ill
>   Charms.
> Be bury'd in those monumental Arms,
> All we can say is, may that Earth lie light
> Upon thy tender Limbs; and so Goodnight.

The Consequences of this ill-judged Union were such as might have been expected. The unhappy Beauty, having for some time been interred in this sepulchral Bed, and exposed to the lascivious Clasps of impotent Leachery, soon declined in Health, and contracted a languishing Indisposition, which Physicians had not Discernment enough to account for. Her Complexion, which had naturally more of the Lilly than the Rose, degenerated into the sallow Hue of Sickness; and her Eyes, which, tho' soft, were sufficiently lively, became faint and unanimated, and seemed to indicate a broken Constitution. Her Physicians had Recourse to a Variety of Remedies, which all proved equally ineffectual; and I am credibly informed, that one of these Sons of *Æsculapius* declared gravely, that the Lady's Disorder had many Symptoms in common with the Chlorosis; but that he did not apprehend that a married Woman could be attacked by that Malady.

The Disorder gaining Ground every Day, it was at last agreed upon, that nothing was so likely to re-establish the Patient's Health as Change of Air: wherefore it was resolved by the Family, that the Lady should be sent to the House of one of her Husband's female Relations, who lived in a distant Part of the Country, remarkable for the Healthiness of its Air. The Proposition was gladly accepted by the new-married Lady; and the more so, because her Husband's Affairs prevented him from accompanying her. The Husband and Wife then agreeing to a short Separation, took Leave of each other with very little Regret, at least on one Side.

Nothing remarkable happened in the Journey; and the sick Lady, for some time after her Arrival, perceived but little Alteration in the State of her Health, notwithstanding the

boasted Salubrity of the Air which she then breathed. If she found somewhat more Satisfaction in the Country than she had done in Town, it was entirely due to the Absence of her Husband. This Satisfaction, however, was not a little diminished by the Importunity of Country Visitants, and the officious Kindness of her Kinswoman.

There happened to be at that time in the Family a young Man, who, tho' his Condition exceeded not that of a Servant, had sometimes shewed a Concern for her Case, which had affected her more than all the Marks of Tenderness she had received from her Relations and Acquaintance, tho' she was too great a Novice to perceive the Impression he made upon her, immediately.

Here I shall beg Leave to make a Digression, in order to prepare the Reader for what is to follow, by a Description of the Person in question.

He was under twenty Years of Age, and somewhat above a middle Stature, exactly shaped, but rather too slender, being not yet arrived at his full Growth. His Deportment was easy, and he had so little of the Air of a Footman, that he might have passed for a Gentleman at *Paris*. His Hair, which was as black as Jet, instead of being concealed in a Bag, adorned his Temples with a natural Flow, superior to all that artificial Grace which every *French* Barber vainly imagines he can give with the Help of a Pair of curling Irons. It was tied with a Ribbon, and fell half way down his Back. His Eyes were Sloe-black, and contained an equal Mixture of Sweetness and Fire. His other Features were regular; and his Complexion, tho' not very ruddy, had a Clearness and Delicacy rarely to be seen in that of a Woman. Add to this, that all his Words and Actions expressed a Sweetness of Temper, that, in some measure, engaged the Affection of every body.

One Evening, that he was sent to call the Lady down to Supper, she found herself so weak, that she could not help leaning upon his Arm; and having expressed some Apprehension of falling, he answered with a Country Simplicity, 'Madam, you are in no Danger of falling, as long as I am with you.'

Whilst she leaned on his Arm, she found her Spirits strangely revived, and her Strength increased to such a Degree, that 'tis probable she could have gone the rest of the Way unsupported;

127

but she was forced by some irresistible Attraction to remain in her former Position.

The next Day, being *Sunday*, her Kinswoman went to Church. Her Footman was unable to attend her, having been taken violently ill the Night before. All the Family was now abroad, except the young Fellow and the Lady above-mentioned. A Sentiment of Gratitude, which will undoubtedly meet with the Approbation of every Reader, who is not a Stranger to the Virtues of Humanity, made the young Lady solicitous about the Health of one, who had contributed in some measure to restore hers. Impelled by this virtuous Passion, she went up to the Room where the young Fellow lay.

Here let us stop, to admire the Humility of a Lady of Fortune, who could so far lose Sight of the Difference of Conditions as to visit a Footman in a Garret! And, tho' the Action may appear somewhat exceptionable to the prudish Part of the Sex, yet, if they reflect that to visit the Sick is enjoined us as a Duty, we are inclined to think, that even they will abate somewhat of their Severity. In fine, she went up, and found the young Fellow stretched on the Bed, tho' in his Clothes. As soon as she appeared, he started up, and Joy sparkled in his Eyes: the sympathetick Matter, which darted from them in Abundance, and with Impetuosity, entered hers, which danced with corresponding Alacrity. Her Complection, at that Instant, seemed to acquire a Bloom, which it could not boast in the most florid State of Health she had ever enjoyed. And such is the Efficacy of the sympathetick Matter in curing certain Disorders, that the young Fellow's Indisposition left him intirely, insomuch that he had Vigour enough to seize the young Lady in his Arms, and throw her on the Bed. She was, perhaps, preparing to complain of this Treatment; but he stopped her Mouth with Kisses. He proceeded then to her Bosom, and rioted anew upon that Seat of Bliss. She had by this time so far forgot her first Design, that, hurried away by some sympathetick Power, she returned his Embraces with equal Ardour; and, in the Struggle of Passion, accidentally unbuttoned his Waistcoat, and * * * * Emboldened hereby, and actuated by a corresponding Operation of the sympathetick Matter, his Hands acquitted themselves so well, that they soon discovered to his Eyes Beauties that surpassed all he had seen before; and increased his Ardour to such a Degree, that * * * *

128

The old Lady, upon her Return, congratulated her Kins-woman upon her looking much better than usual, telling her, that she would certainly recover her Health in a short time, since the Air of that Place was the most healthy in the Kingdom.

That she did recover it soon after, is certain; tho' we ap-prehend, that several Interviews, concerted between her and the young Fellow, might have contributed to this Recovery as much as the healthy Air of the Place.

Whether her Return to Town, and to her Husband, might have caused a Relapse; or whether she might, in order to preserve her Health, have had Recourse to certain Expedients sometimes used by the Ladies, are Points concerning which we could never acquire any certain Information.

THE

JOYS

OF

HYMEN,

OR, THE

CONJUGAL DIRECTORY:

A

POEM,

In THREE BOOKS.

Here Love his golden Shafts employs, here lights
His conftant Lamp, and waves his purple Wings.

MILTON.

LONDON.

Printed for D. DAVIS in *Paternofter-Row*.
M.DCC.LXVIII.

A MARRIAGE GUIDE

THE aged dame to venery inclin'd,
With a dry body and salacious mind,
Whose swimming eyes distil eternal brine,
Whose Indian teeth the burnish'd jett outshine;
A thousand lovers court, to win her gold,
Whose youthful veins at sight of her grow cold,
And, from the twinkling of her letchrous eyes
Presage, whose fortune waits the golden prize:
Some cunning youth, more artful than the rest,
Finds a short passage to her aged breast;
But, when possest of all, his passion flags,
And his discourse is bent on wanton hags,
With dotage, and with matrimony cloy'd,
The dow'r too little – wife too much enjoy'd;
He gives himself the liberty to rove
Through all the paths of habitable love,
And grants to others, what she thinks her due,
His wealth, his company, and raptures too;
Then jealousy and rage, her transports rouse,
And she upbraids him with his slighted vows:
To drink the fatal draught she turns her mind,
A prey to grief and racking cares resign'd.
Would great religion leave to nature's voice,
To cull the pleasures, with unbounded choice:
Then each, intuitive, by instinct led,
No more would curse the sacred marriage-bed.
But heav'n such lawless liberty denies,
Ordaining sacred rites, and solemn ties.
Happy the pair, who not by custom join'd,
But noble instinct, marry in the mind;
Who, truely one, divide in equal shares
Their nightly pleasures, and their daily cares.

THE virgin sooner than the boy may sport,
And the fond, pleasing name of mother court:
Observe the tokens of the gentle fire:
When first the maiden glows with fierce desire,

A florid crimson decorates her cheeks,
And the soft wishes of the bosom speaks;
Her panting breasts emit a thousand sighs,
And wanton ardour brightens in her eyes:
With faultring limbs, she meets the vig'rous boy,
Melts at his touch, and trembles to enjoy,
Sinks, with pleas'd transports in a lover's arms,
And, blushing, mourns her yet unrifled charms.

WHEN, the ripe youth is conscious of delight,
(Pleas'd with involuntary acts each night)
The real joys of love, he then may taste,
Lest the pure stores of nature run to waste.

IF those who try an hymeneal cause,
Observe these rules, these statutes, and these laws;
The Cytherean art would be refin'd,
To propagate a noble, gen'rous mind.

THE guests retir'd, the youth with eager haste
Seeks his bright spouse, who sighs to be embrac'd;
With ardent looks beholds her swimming eyes,
And glowing cheeks, where purple charms arise;
Her heaving breasts, of purest snowy hue,
Her ev'ry charm his lovesick heart inspires,
And fills with love, and eager, fond desires.
While yet he hangs upon the melting kiss,
And sighing, panting, burns for higher bliss:
'Haste, haste, (he cries) unloose the virgin zone,
And let my charming bride be all my own.'

– RASH youth desist! – Thy joys a while forbear,
And think thy future offspring claims thy care;
Sooth thy fair spouse! With gentle kisses warm,
While glowing blushes heighten ev'ry charm;
Let each delight thy raptur'd bosom prove;
But yet delay the last dear task of love:
Fresh from the Festal board, if thus you meet,
Not long the transport, nor the bliss complete.
While love's warm balm in vain you seek to pour,
An unconcocted, tepid, drizzling show'r:

For hence no males replete with gen'rous fire
Shall spring; no beauteous damsels call you sire.
Weak, foul, mis-shap'd, soon verging tow'rds an end,
Are the sad offspring which such rites attend;
For sages say, the warm and active juice,
Which purple wines and CERES gifts produce;
The kindly strength which feeds the genial flame
Of love, or nourishes the vital frame;
All these (a rude and indigested heap)
Digestive pow'rs will ripen while you sleep;
Strain through unnumber'd tubes the flowing tide,
And blood from chyle, and sperm from blood divide.
Soft perspiration through the pores distills
Superfluous moisture; livelier vigour fills
The turgid veins; till fresh from downy rest,
Calm peace and health reign equal in your breast.
Then urge your suit, around the fair entwine:
In am'rous folds, and close embraces join;
Joyful complete what ardent you began,
And stamp an image worthy of a man.

YE too, fond wives, who, in excess of joy,
Snatch at the sweets, and too much heat employ;
Invent not various ways to taste the bliss,
But soft and gentle take the melting kiss.
Be modest; nor to shew the woman's force,
Disgrace the sex, and spoil the genial course:
Obey great Nature, all her laws revere,
And she shall make your ev'ry joy sincere.
Forgive me, nymphs, if by my subject led,
I follow Nature to her fountain-head.

IN close recesses, hid from curious eyes,
Beneath a shade the blissful region lies;
A rising eminence the vale surrounds,
And justly marks the limitary bounds
On ev'ry side: beneath cool fountains flow,
Which water all the fertile fields below:
A thwarting line divides the middle space:
Here sport the boys, and *there* the virgin plays.

A shady walk, adjoining to the grove,
Leads thence to the delightful bow'rs of Love.
The various mazes you with pleasure trace,
While lovely streams irriguate all the place,
Here VENUS sports upon the smiling plain;
Here Nature first begins her active reign.
As when the rustic thirsts to cheer his soul,
With large potations from the flowing bowl,
So gapes the field, to catch the balmy dews,
Which genial Nature's kindly pow'rs infuse:
The welcome moisture fills each swelling seed;
Blossoms and buds, and richest crops succeed.

Vilario having found out *Camillo's* amorous Vein, and by his last Conversation removed from his Mind the Impression of his Tutor's Rigidity, soon gained upon his Temper, and became his entire Confidante; so that *Camillo* was under no manner of Restraint, but frankly communicated all his Inclinations to *Vilario*, who took care to gratify him in every Respect, and permitted him to run into all the Extravagance of unbridled Youth, observing no other Decorum, but what was necessary to conceal their Course of Life from such of *Camillo's* Relations as they were obliged to visit, before whom, both the Tutor and Pupil practised all the Grimace of Virtue and Piety, passing upon them, by the most exquisite Dissimulation, for two of the soberest Gentlemen of the Age. They even carried their Hypocrisy so far, as to be frequently seen at Church, not only on *Sundays*, but on Week Days; and behaved on these Occasions with all the outward Marks of the most sincere Devotion, though in their hearts, they, perhaps, cursed the Parson, and wished the Service at the Devil. They were obliged to this kind of Behaviour, in order to obtain and preserve the Esteem of a rich Citizen and near Kinsman of *Camillo's*, who being himself very devotedly inclined, from a small Tincture of Fanaticism he had imbibed in his Youth, during the last Years of the Usurpation, when the whole Kingdom was possessed with a kind of religious Madness, was mightily pleased to find the Marks of Grace so pregnant in his young Kinsman, and on that Account, and to encourage the young Saint in his pious Courses, was profuse of his Purse, which was a strong Temptation to *Camillo* to continue his Hypocrisy, because his other less religious Exercises demanded more Money than the Allowance his Father made him would admit of, though that was very liberal. Therefore, when ever his Cash ran low, he went to a Church in the City, where he was sure to meet with his old Kinsman; there he put on a demure Look for half an Hour, and repeated the Responses with a zealous and reverent Spirit of Devotion; which so charmed the Heart of the Old Miser, that he constantly invited him home, and recruited those Pockets, which had been emptied the Night before, not with Acts of Charity and

Religion, but in Company with a Knot of such pious Youths as himself, who, for the Improvement of their Morals by the vertuous Conversation of the Girls of the Town, used frequently to spend their Evenings together.

But *Camillo* did not grow profligate all at once; his Tutor in Iniquity was obliged to initiate him by slow and insensible Degrees; for to speak the Truth, except a natural Proneness to the Fair Sex, *Camillo* had no constitutional Vice to struggle with, and the Care and Conversation of his first Tutor had instilled into his tender Mind the seeds and first Principles of many good Qualities, which in Time might have been cherished to great and good Purposes, and took *Vilario* some pains to eradicate. *Camillo* had a natural Openness of Temper, a strong Antipathy to Falsehood and Prevarication, and an innate Veneration for every Thing relating to Religion. These were Virtues that stood in the way of *Vilario's* Views upon him, yet he durst not attack them openly in Person, but led his Pupil in to such Company as by Degrees laughed him out of every Thing that might be a Check upon the Gratification of any sensual Appetite.

After *Vilario* had discovered *Charlotta's* Plot upon *Camillo*, as I have observed, he kept him out of her Reach, not out of any personal Regard to the Honour or Interest of his Pupil, but for his own Interest and Reputation, which he knew would suffer if he permitted such a Step to be taken while under his Direction. And least he might be drawn into the same Snare by some one who had more Skill in laying and conducting a matrimonial Plot, he railed against Marriage with all the Wit and Malice he was Master of, and represented that State to his young Charge in the most hideous Colours, till he had wrought him up to the greatest Aversion for it. This Point gained, *Vilario* became less cautious of carrying his Pupil into all sorts of Company and Conversation, particularly such as he himself generally kept when he laid aside his virtuous Airs, and appeared in his own natural Colours. These consisted chiefly of young Rakes of Quality, who had formerly profited under the Tuition of this hopeful travelling Governor; Players, Poets, Musicians, Old Bauds and young Whores. He had Acquaintance of all Classes, and set Hours for attending their Meetings at different Places of the Town, which he managed so artfully, that though he was every Night in some Scene of Debauchery or other, yet he came so seldom to the same Place, that he escaped being observed to be one of their Society.

He at first introduced *Camillo* to the Class of them who observed the greatest Decorum in their Debauches; from them to the next Degree, till he had travelled through all the Scenes of Vice and Folly our Metropolis is able to exhibit, and *Camillo* in a few Weeks became so expert a Scholar in this University of Vice, that he excelled most of his Fellow-Students in Iniquity; could walk in that dark Path without Leading-strings, and was in a fair way of groping out his way to the Devil without the help of a Guide. We shall only take a short View of some of his Rambles in *England*, and then proceed to his Exploits in Foreign Parts, on which the short Stay he made at *London*, had great Influence.

A Night or two after his Affair with the Widow's Daughter was blown up, *Vilario* and he walking in the *Mall* at *St James's*, were met by an Acquaintance of the former's, who seemed to be a Man of Three-score, but was dressed like a Boy of Fifteen, and what between the Antiquity of his Phiz, and the Youthfulness of his Dress and Conservation, he made in *Camillo's* Eyes a very ridiculous Appearance. However, as *Vilario* shewed him Respect and there appeared a great Intimacy betwixt them, he refrained treating him with that Contempt which his Appearance created in him, and received the Compliments the old Beau made him on *Vilario's* introducing them to each other, with as much Politeness as the small Knowledge he had yet of the Town would permit him; Captain *Wearwell*, for that was the Beau's Name, grew all of a sudden mighty fond of *Camillo*, and by now and then throwing in a small Dash of Flattery, against which few young Men are very well armed, got the better of his first Prepossession, and in two or three Lengths of the *Mall*, from the most contemptible ridiculous Animal in Life, he became in our young Traveller's Eyes, the most accomplished, obliging, complaisant Gentleman alive. He asked *Camillo* if he had seen any of the publick Diversions, or if his Tutor had introduced him to any of the choice Spirits of the Town. I have been, replied *Camillo*, at the Play, the Opera, and Masquerade, and was very well entertained at them, but that he was yet a Stranger to such good Company as he had mentioned, amongst whom he supposed such a Country Rustic would make but an aukward Figure, which he supposed was the Reason *Vilario* had not yet carried him into Assemblies where the Conversation might be too polite for him to share in—which, however, he should be glad of, in hopes they would have Good-nature enough to put up with his Ignorance, till, by copying from them, he might so far improve himself, as at length to become supportable. Why, returned the old Beau, *Vilario* has greatly injured you, and robbed the *Beau Monde* of a great deal of Pleasure which they might already have reaped from your Conversation: Indeed, Sir, you are too severe upon yourself; your Mien, your Dress, and every Thing about you, pardon the Liberty I take of saying this to your Face, Sir, has quite the genteel and courtly Air of *St James's*. I could not think it possible that such Accomplishments can be acquired in the Country; but some are born with happy Talents, and besides, you have fallen into good Hands; *Vilario* has seen so much of the World, that but a Week's Conversation with him, polishes more than a Twelve-Month's Travel. Well, *Camillo*, I prophesy you will be the Darling of the Ladies, and make more Holes in their Hearts than there are Patches on their Faces: Egad! – But you shall go with us to *Locket's* to-night, where a Set of Smarts are to meet, and are afterwards to make the Grand Tour, which must be high Diversion for one who has not seen the manner in which we Men of Pleasure live. You have, hitherto, Sir, amused yourself in scouring after a poor Hare or a Fox, over Hills, Dales, and Five-Bar Gates, in eminent Danger of your Neck; and then, when come Home, been obliged to pass the Evening in the dull Repetition of the mighty Exploits of *Ringwood* and *Jowler*; and the Height of your Pleasure was toasting the Squire's cherry-cheeked Daughter, in dull *October*, or sophisticated Port: but now, my Hero, the Scene is changed; you pass the whole Day in a round of soft circling Delights, where every Sense is ravished, and the Soul knows no Satiety from the infinite Variety of substantial Joy; and then, my Boy, instead of Hares and Foxes, we make War upon more noxious Animals, the Constables and Watch, and instead of Coney-Warrens and Ferret Holes, we demolish Bawdy-Houses, unrig the Girls, and play a thousand other pleasant Frolicks, to which the whole Generation of Fox-hunters are utter Strangers, and cannot conceive the most distant Idea of the dear Pleasure which we enjoy in these Midnight Sallies.

This Description of a Town Ramble, had too much of Novelty in it not to take the Fancy of our young Adventurer: He had conceived a *high* Notion of the polite Accomplishments of Captain *Wearwell*, and was eager to merit those Applauses he had so liberally bestowed upon him, and to be initated into that Society, whose Pleasures were so much refined, that they quite surpassed his rustic Apprehensoin of Things; therefore you may suppose the Scene changed from the *Mall* to *Locket's*, where an expensive Supper, and plenty of generous Wine, gave fresh Vigour to the youthful Imagination, and stifled all former Notions of Temperance and rational Pleasures. The Company, by a Whisper, were made acquainted with the Quality of our young Squire, and his Address and Air were sufficient to let them into the Secret of his being a Novice in the Town, and all its Ways; they received him with abundance of Complaisance, praised with one side of their Faces, while with the other they laughed at the aukward Simplicity of his Manners. Some of them were inclinable to make Merry with him, and to play off their Wit at him, as the Butt of the Company, but *Vilario's* Presence kept them within Bounds, he not caring to allow them to carry Matters too far, for fear of discouraging his Pupil, whom he intended to engage into a Liking for all the mad Frolicks of that thoughtless Class of Mortals, as most suitable to his own Taste, and the Designs he had upon him. *Camillo* behaved pretty well, and took some Sallies of Raillery which were now and then played off against him, for Wit, and Arguments of the Regard the Company had for him; for he thought they honoured him by permitting him to be of their Society, thought the Group consisted of younger Brothers who lived by sharping, disbanded Captains, debauched Poets, and superannuated Players; but such as they were, he thought them the best Company in the World. After some Hours spent in Riot, Noise and Nonsense, they set about their Grand Tour, and prepared the mighty Enterprize of demolishing Lamps, beating the Watch, and scouring the Streets. Capt. *Wearwell* was Commander in Chief and led the Van, while *Vilario* brought up the Rear with his Pupil, who wanted Experience enough to be trusted in a more advanced Station. The first House they entered was a noted *Bagnio*, where they met with a Covey of Town Partridges, which *Camillo* liked better than all he had ever drawn a Net over in the Country, and amongst them Miss M—— the famous Posture Girl, whose Presence put our Company of Ramblers upon the Crotchet of shewing their new Associate a Scene, of which he had never so much as dreamed before.

They were shewed a large Room, Wine was brought in, the Drawer dismissed, and after a Bumper the Ladies were ordered to prepare. They immediately stripped stark naked, and mounted themselves on the middle of the Table. *Camillo* was greatly surprised at this Apparatus, and not less puzzled in guessing for what Purpose the Girls had posted themselves on that Eminence. They were clean limbed, fresh complectioned, and had Skins as white as the driven Snow, which was heightened by the jet-black Colour of their Hair. They had very good Faces, and the natural Blush which glowed on their Cheeks (in spite of the Custom of their Trade, on seeing so many Men fix their Eyes on that Part which all other Woman chuse to hide) rendered them in *Camillo's* Mind, finished Beauties, and fit to rival *Venus* herself, who could not appear more lovely, had she thus sat for her Picture to *Apelles*. From viewing their Faces, he bashfully cast his Eyes on the Altar of Love, which he never had so fair a View of as at this present time. He had seen, it's true, the Secret, though only budding, Beauties of his Cousin Maria, and been very familiar with those of the Laundry Maid in the Country: but the Parts of the celebrated Posture Girl, had something about them which attracted his attention more than any thing he had either felt or seen. The Throne of Love was thickly covered with Jet-black Hair, at least a Quarter of a Yard long, which she artfully spread asunder, to display the Entrance into the Magic Grotto. The uncommon Figure of this bushy Spot, afforded a very odd sort of Amusement to *Camillo*, which was more heightened by the rest of the Ceremony which these Wantons went through. They each filled a Glass of Wine, and laying themselves in an extended Posture placed their Glasses on the Mount of *Venus*, every Man in Company drinking off the Bumper, as it stood on that tempting Protuberance, while the Wenches were not wanting in their lascivious Motions, to heighten the Diversion. Then they went thro' the several Postures and Tricks made use to raise debilitated Lust, when cloyed with natural Enjoyment, and afterwards obliged poor *Camillo* to shoot the Bridge, and pass under the warm Cataracts, which discomposed him more than if he had been overset in a *Gravesend* Wherry. However, tho' it raised the Laugh of the whole Company, he bore this Frolick with a good deal of Patience, as he was told it was necessary for all new Members to be thus initiated into the Mysteries of their Society. *Camillo* began now to be disgusted at the prodigious Impudence of the Women; he found in himself no more of that uneasy Emotion he felt at their first setting out, and was desirous of the Company's dismissing them; but his Companions would not part with them, till they had gone through the whole of their Exercise; the Nymphs, who raised a fresh Contribution on every new Discovery of their impudent Inventions, required no Entreaties to gratify the young Rakes, but proceeded, without the least Sense of Shame, to shew them how far Human Nature could debase itself.

Their last Exploit inflamed these Sons of Debauchery so much, that they proposed, as a Conclusion of the Scene, that each Man should chuse his Posture, and go through what they had seen only imitated before. But this was a Step the Nymphs would not comply with, it being the Maxim of these Damsels, never to admit of the Embraces of Men, for fear of spoiling their Trade. This very much surprized *Camillo*, who from their former Behaviour, perswaded himself there could not be invented any Species of Wickedness with which they would not comply, for the Sake of Money; and though before this their Refusal, their abandoned Obscenity had quite stifled all thoughts of lying with them, yet now his Desires were as strong as if they had been modest Virgins, and he had seen nothing of their Wantonness; so that he became as earnest to oblige them to comply, as any Man of the Company. But the Girls remained inflexible, dressed themselves in the greatest Hurry, and could be prevailed on by no Entreaties to stay longer in the Company. The Gentlemen, who believed it all Grimace, and that they stood off only to enhance their Price, offered what Money they pleased; but that had no Effect; and one of them, who seemed to be a Girl of an uncommon Genius, addressed herself to the Company in this manner: 'Gentlemen, I cannot blame you for having a very mean Opinion of us, and for believing that after the Scenes we have gone through to-night, we have no remains of Virtue or Modesty left, but I can assure you I have as great an Avertion to Whoring (and I may venture to say as much for those that are here with me) as some Women who are nicely scrupulous in every other Respect; and, however strange you may think it, my Mind is as little tainted by the Life I am obliged to lead, and have pursued from my infancy, as it was before I was capable of knowing the Distinction of the Sexes. Perhaps, Gentlemen, if you would permit me to give you a short Sketch of my History, you would be inclined to think me sincere, and that it is needless for you to persevere in your present Intention.'

This Preamble raised our Gentlemen's Curiosity, and with one accord they agreeing to hear her Story, she began as follows:

'I was born, Gentlemen, of honest Parents, but had the Misfortune to lose them before I could be sensible of my Loss. I was but turned of Eight when both Father and Mother died, in a short Space after one another, and left me to the Care of an Aunt, without any other Obligation to support me, but what arose from the Tyes of Blood, for all their Effects were scarce sufficient to bury them. But alas! our being so nearly related, was not sufficient to induce my Aunt to be long solicitous about my Welfare; it is true, she allowed me a bare Subsistence, for a Year or two, but without troubling her Head about cultivating my Mind, or forming my Morals, of which she had naturally herself but very loose Notions. I was then remarkably well limbed, had a good Complexion, and tolerable Features, with a natural Liveliness in my Temper, which engaged me to my Aunt more than Nearness of Blood; my forward Prattle diverted her, and she indulged me in every rompish Trick I could invent, without considering what were their Tendencies; she carried me to see her Neighbours, a Set of Gossips, who had not all the nicest Notions of Virtue, and who were pleased with my Forwardness, however indecently expressed. I was taught a number of licentious Songs, of which I did not then understand the Meaning, which used to set the old Women, her Cronies, in such a Titter, that I was thought the best Company in the World, and was loaded with Caresses, Toys, and Sugar-Plumbs, for what I ought to have been severely chastised.

'I went on improving in this kind of Education, till I was eleven Years of Age, when my Aunt married her second Husband, for she was all this Time a Widow. He proved a covetous Hunks, who grudged me every Bit of Victuals I ate, and wanted my Aunt to turn me over to the Parish. She was doatingly fond of him, and though she liked me well enough for my forward Tricks, yet she would have been glad to have been rid of me in any Shape, except to the Parish, which her Pride would not let her think of; therefore she made shift to keep me for some Months, in hopes that some Opportunity would offer to shake me off in a manner more agreeable to her Pride.

'At this Juncture a famous Rope-Dancer came to the Village where we lived, and put up at the House of one of my Aunt's Intimates, where I had frequently been. All our Family went to see the Rope-Dancing, and my Aunt and I staid with the Woman of the House after the Shew was over, and the Dancer was admitted to drink with them after the Fatigue of her Exercise. They soon become familiarly merry together, and I was desired to add to their Mirth by a Bawdy Song, which I humoured so by my Action, as to engage the Good-Will and Attention of the Rope-Dancer. She commended my Parts, and at last ventured to observe that I was a well-limbed active Girl, and if rightly brought up, might make my Fortune by following her Profession; but, added she, I am afraid she's too forward, she would be too soon debauched: that's the only Rub she could meet with. No more passed that Night; the Gossips parted, but the next Day my Aunt sent for the Dancer, and, in short, I was bound Apprentice for seven Years to learn Postures and Rope Dancing.

'If I had any Modesty before this Period, it easily wore off under the Tuition of my new Mistress, who found me an apt Scholar in learning her Postures. I soon began to think that there was no more harm in exposing myself before Men, than before Women: However, as I grew up, I was taught that nothing could be a greater Misfortune to me in the Way of my Profession, than to have any criminal Conversation with the Men. This Lesson I learned before I well understood the Basis it was founded on, and so I found myself guarded against the Evil, when Experience taught me what I was cautioned against: and though when in that Woman's Service I exposed myself Naked, and in many obscene Postures in some Select Companies, yet being so much accustomed to vicious Tricks in my Infancy,

they inspired in me no more loose Thoughts, than if I had been reading a Common-Prayer-Book; it was purely mechanical, a Scene in which my Body was only concerned, but in no measure influenced my Morals. I pleased my Mistress, and got her a great deal of Money, for the first four Years I was with her, by the many Feats of Activity she had learned me; but after that Time, my Joints became less pliable, and I found myself unable to go through the many monkey Tricks she put into her Bills, to allure the wondering Crowd. She saw I could not help it, and therefore was not angry with me, though she was concerned to see that she would be forced to hire one to supply my Place in those Parts of her Shew which I could no longer exhibit: But to make up for the Loss she had in that Respect, she resolved to make Sale of that Commodity, which she had hitherto so often told me it was my greatest Interest to preserve; and fancying that I would make but small Opposition to her Will, without consulting me, she made Sale of my Virginity to a Country Justice in *Devonshire*. We were then shewing away in a Village belonging to that Gentleman, who was an old Batchelor; and he, after the Bargain was struck, sent for my Mistress and me to his House, which was at one End of the Village. We had no Reason to be displeased with the Entertainment of the old Justice; for we were treated with all the Respect due to Persons of a much higher Rank, and I was favoured by the good 'Squire with particular Marks of Esteem. After Supper I was surprized that we were conducted into separate Apartments, as we used in all Places to be Bedfellows; I began to be apprehensive of some Danger, and desired the Servant, who lighted me to my Chamber, to tell my Mistress I wanted to speak with her before she went to sleep. My Mistress came in a few Minutes, and asked me what I wanted with her; I told her, I was afraid to lie alone in that great old House, which might be haunted with Spirits for aught I knew, and would rather be her Bedfellow as usual, or go to the Inn and lie there: Child, say she, what do you mean? Who knows but the good Justice may have some Business with you before Morning? if he has, it would be ill Manners to disappoint him; in short, I believe he has a Month's Mind for a Maidenhead, and I fancy may bid pretty high; if he does, you may let the old Fellow have his Will; I am sure you will not be the worse for it to-morrow. I started at the Proposal, as if I had

146

trod upon a Serpent, and told her, after what Lessons I had heard her give me on that Subject, I was surprized to hear her talk at such a Rate; that for my part, to carry on her Business, I had gone all the Lengths she had hitherto desired me, but was determined to take her own Advice, and not go one Step further. Hey dey! replied my Mistress, half in a Rage, what, Madam, do you pretend to give yourself Airs of Chastity! You, who have exposed all you have to half the Kingdom! sure you are be-witched! It is true, I advised you to keep your Maidenhead for fear of spoiling your Shape, and rendering you useless in our Way; but now you are grown so already, the Caution is need-less; and as your Fruit is now ripe, you ought to make the most of it before it grows too mellow; you must some time or other bring the Toy to Market, and I doubt not but Mr Justice will give you your full Price, and leave you as marketable as before; therefore, Hussey, cease your blubbering, receive the 'Squire as you ought, and shew no more Coyness than is necessary to squeeze his Pockets. So saying, she whipt out of the Room, took the Key on the out-side, and locked me in.

'I acknowledge, Gentlemen, you have Reason to believe I am entertaining you with a Romance; but more so if I should repeat the Agony I felt at this Instant. Incredible as it may seem to you, nothing is, however, more true than this Circumstance: Even now, when better acquainted with the loosest Scenes of Vice, I shudder at the Thoughts of what I felt. I do not say my Senti-ments were delicate on that Subject, or that the Thoughts of Honour, or Dread of Shame influenced my Mind; I had long accustomed myself to think with Indifference of what other Women are most ashamed. I had no Character to lose, I had Sense enough to think *that* bad enough in the Eye of the cen-sorious World, which, ignorant of the Heart, judges only by the shallowest Appearance; but I found something within me, which started at the Thoughts of Prostitution, and made me dread it worse than Death. I then reflected how often, when I have been fretting myself at the mean Opinion most of my Sex had of me, for exposing myself in the manner I did, and how they looked on me as one abandoned to all Sense of Virtue; I then reflected, I say, how often I had comforted myself with this Thought, that however abandoned I appeared to the World, yet my Mind was a Stranger to many of those Vices I knew most of my rigid Censurers were guilty of in private, and that I could boast to myself I had preserved my real Chastity. But now that I was in a fair way of losing the Fruits of all my Care to a lascivious old Miser, I fancied to myself, that my Chastity was much more valuable to me, and the preservation of it a much greater Virtue, than to other Women, brought up according to all the strict Rules of Decency and Decorum. I had as much Flesh and Blood in my Constitution as most Women: the Scenes I acted, the Conversation I heard, the Company I kept, were all strong Provocatives, and capable of setting every wanton Desire afloat, to destroy every virtuous Resolution; yet I went through the fiery Trial, and preserved not only my Person but my Mind in a great measure free from the Stains of lawless Lust, while those who thought me abandoned, perhaps owed their Chastity to the Frigidity of their Constitution, or want of Temptation and Opportunity, for many yield without half the Repugnance I felt in my own Mind, without half the Struggles I opposed to the Attempts of the Justice. But I had still another Motive to determine me to be true to myself at that time, which though it shewed more of the Woman in me, yet it heightened my present Distress; and that was the Affection I had contracted for a young Man who travelled in our Company; I had plighted my Faith to him, that as soon as I was disposed to alter my Condition, or part with my Maidenhead, it should be his upon honest Terms; but we both proposed to suspend our Design, till we were in a Condition of living above the scandalous Occupation we were now engaged in. All these Thoughts crowded on my Mind at once, and sunk into the most terrible Despair; for I concluded my Mistress had sold me to the old Letcher. I ran to the Door, and tried to unlock it, to see if I could get out of the House, but that was impossible; however I espied a Bolt on the Inside, which I immediately Shot, and then barricaded the Door with all the Tables and Chairs in the Room, resolving, that since I could not get out, no Body should get in. Being now secure in my own Imagination, and trusting to the Strength of the Garrison, I undressed and went to Bed, pleased that I had disappointed their wicked Intentions for that Night, and trusting that Providence would put something in my Head to dissipate my Fears against next Day. In about half an Hour I was just dropping asleep, when I heard the Key turn in the Door, and a Foot push against it: but all stood firm, and I was diverting myself with the Thoughts how vexed his Worship would be, that he should be obliged to hug his Pillow for that Night, after promising himself the mumbling of a Maidenhead of Fifteen. After some few Bounces at the Door to no purpose, the Noise suddenly ceased and I turned myself to rest, when to my inexpressible Surprize, I saw the old Gentleman enter in his Night-Gown and Slippers, with a Candle in his Hand, through a Door which opened at the Foot of the Bed, and which I had not before observed. I shrieked out as if I had seen a Ghost, for that indeed was the first Notion that struck me; but I was soon convinced that the Apparition was not purely spiritual; for setting the Candle down, he threw off his Night-Gown, jumped into Bed as nimbly as a Boy of Eighteen, clasped me fast in his withered Arms, and stifled me with his odious Kisses, for the old Rogue stunk at that time, or I fancied he did, like any Goat. I endeavoured all I could to get from him, and made Noise enough to have raised the Dead; but the worthy Justice did not mind my Cries, Threats, Curses, or Entreaties, he was for going the shortest way to storm the Citadel, when he found coaxing would not do, and I observed by his not being concerned at my Outcries, that I could expect no Relief from without; I therefore left off my Squawling, and reserved my Strength to oppose the Enemy Force to Force, who seemed ready to enter the Breach. But when I put down my Hand to oppose his Entrance, for he had already penetrated the Outworks, I found he had exhausted all his Ammunition in the Storm, and had not one Grain of Powder left to carry on the Attack, if I had left the Fort without a Guard: What I now laid hold on, gave me the Idea of a Snail that had been trod upon, shrinking back into its Shell. I was glad to find my Enemy so impotent, for I begun to find my Strength fail with struggling and bawling, and therefore considered with myself, that it was the Thing I was contending for, and not the Name, and since my old Hero was in no Condition to do me any Injury, it was needless to make Opposition, as his Inability was Guard sufficient to my Virtue. I made my Repulses weaker and weaker by Degrees, and at last, as if quite exhausted, left him the open Field. Overjoyed that I had removed all Impediments, he made another Push, vigorous enough to have alarmed any poor Virgin less experienced than me. But alas! he

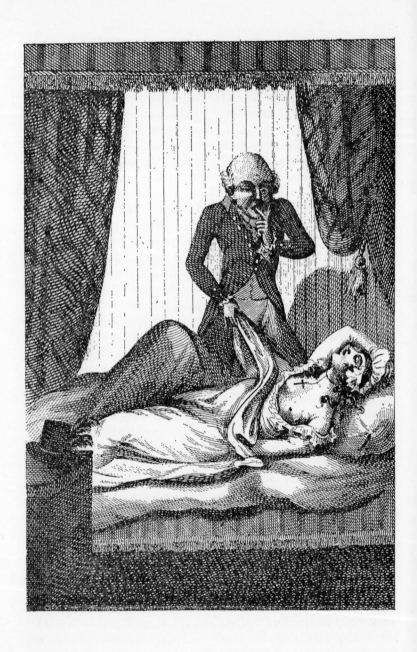

was still as far from the Point as ever: He bobb'd against the Breach, but could not move one Inch over the Threshold. He repeated his Efforts, but always in vain; his Forces were now weakened, and dispirited, beyond all possibility of rallying. Quite confounded that he was so baffled, he started from his Post, as if he had been stung by a Nettle, bounced out of Bed, put on his Night-Gown, and vanished in an instant, without speaking one Word. Pleased with my Deliverance from Age, Imposture, and Letchery, I slept soundly for the rest of the Night, and in the Morning got up earlier than ordinary, went to the Village, where I met my Sweetheart, and told him every Syllable that past, without concealing the minutest Circumstance. We both joined in cursing the old Bawd our Mistress and laughing at the poor Justice. But we thought it necessary to consult what was to be done to avoid such Accidents for the future, and we could think of no other Expedient to free me from the Danger of being sold to the first that would give Money enough for me, but to leave the Service. This Thought was no sooner mentioned, than it was put into Execution, for that very Day I set out for *Gosport*, took shipping there for *London*, where I arrived without any Accident, accompanied by the young Man, who treated me with as much Modesty as if I had been his Sister. We soon got into a Company of Strollers, who were exhibiting at *Sadler's Wells*, where I had not been above a Month, when Mr —— the famous Painter, sent for me; I wondered what he might want with me, but was not above answering his Message. I went, and he told me he had a Proposal to make to me, which if I accepted, would turn much to my Advantage; if I did not, he hoped I would not take the Offer amiss, since he had no intention to affront but to serve me. I begged him to name his Proposal without any further Preamble. In a word, his Design was to make use of me as a Figure in a private Academy of Painters and was directed to me by Sir *James Thornhill*, who had the chief Management of that Affair. I was by no means startled at the Proposal, because while with my Mistress, I had frequently, to humour select Companies of young Rakes, acted my Postures quite naked; therefore I made little or no Hesitation to engage with the Academy, who allowed me more than I could get by Rope-Dancing; and they made it an express Condition in their Engagement with me, that I was to have no Commerce with Men: an injunction I observed sacredly for seven Years; for so long I stood as a Pattern for the use of that Society. During this Time I lived privately, and respected by all who knew me; for I had shaken off all Acquaintance with the Strollers, and had taken Lodgings in a remote Corner, and passed for a young Lady from the Country. I never went out, but in a Chair to the Academy, which was only three Times a Week. The rest of my Time I employed in reading, so that my Landlady justly looked upon me as a very sober and virtuous Person. But in about seven Years, the Affairs of that Society took a different Turn, and I was left to shift for myself and had nothing now to depend on but what I had from young Painters, for standing to them at their own Houses, which was not sufficient to maintain me. My Acquaintance lay among the Painters, and some of them, who knew my Difficulties, in order to help me, have sent for me to go to Taverns, where I only shewed myself naked without going through any further Obscenities. This happening often, and in so promiscuous Company, one told another, and I was sent for continually, till at length I made myself too common, and, to get Bread, was obliged to fall into all the Tricks which you have seen, yet still I have preserved my Chastity, and am resolved to do so till I can be settled in some better way of Life.'

The Company were mightily pleased with the History the Posture-Girl gave of herself. By this Time their Fire was in some measure abated, and they did not insist so violently upon their first Proposal, but permitted the Ladies to depart, and were contented to send for some less reserved, and who had not such odd Notions of Chastity. And now our Revellers proposed to adjourn their Ramble for the Night, and to spend the Remainder of it by lying in State, that is, each with a Brace of Girls. The ladies were sent for, and every Gentleman made his Election by Ballotting, and then retired to their respective Apartments with their *Bona Roba's*.

Camillo liked a Girl well enough, but he found no great Stomach for two or three at a time; and had so much Country Bashfulness left, that he scarce knew how to behave between them. But these sort of Creatures know how to banish Modesty, and every thing else that tends to baulk their View; they placed our young Traveller in the middle between them, and used all the Tricks and Freedom they could invent to animate him to Action. *Camillo* had nothing frigid in his Constitution, but he found himself so much embarrassed how to please two at a time, and shocked with the Thoughts of having a Witness to an Action he had always observed the greatest Privacy in, that he was little better than the old Justice, for the first Quarter of an Hour he was in Bed, and frequently wished them both at the Devil; for to his other Perplexity was added the Shame to be thought incapable, a Secret he could not hide from their busy Fingers, which were officiously employed to raise the pendent Member; and the more he was vexed, the less capable he was of helping himself. But at last, the Heat of Blood got the better of his Embarassment. Their warm Dalliance brought the Spirits to their proper Channels, when *Camillo* had begun to despair of finding his Vigour return. He now resolved not to lose the Opportunity, by deliberating which of the two he should begin with, but taking the one that lay most convenient, he gave a sufficient Proof of his Virility, which some Moments before there was some Reason to call in Question; and before Morning he gave each of them Reason enough to be pleased with his Manhood, as they were with his Liberality, before they went away; for he tipped each of them a Yellow Boy, treated them with Breakfast, and sent them home in their Chairs. This he did very early, and got home to his Lodgings without calling for his Companions; for he began to be crop-sick, and was afraid of a fresh Debauch if he staid.

Vilario came home about an Hour after and told *Camillo* that the Company were charmed with his Behaviour and Conversation, and had made him promise, in his Name, to meet them at Night in the same Place; but *Camillo* desired to be excused for that Night, as he found himself a little out of Order, and durst not venture too much at once on his Constitution, before he had seasoned it by Degrees. It was not proper for the Tutor to urge too much against so good an Excuse, and therefore gave him a Respite for that Night.

In a Day or two after, *Camillo* met with the same Set, and made the Tour of the Bawdy-Houses in general, and by that means became acquainted with the Manners and Customs of the Hundreds of *Drury Lane* and *Covent-Garden*. They compleated their Ramble by breaking a sufficient number of Lamps,

and the Heads of as many Watchmen, and were marching home in Triumph, when they encountered, at *Temple Bar*, a Posse of the Watch carrying off a Gentleman, who appeared by his Dress to be of some Fashion. Our Gallants thought themselves in Honour bound to relieve the Distressed, and boldly attacked the Guard, who were put into some Disorder at the first Onset; but a fresh Supply coming from the Neighbouring Garrisons, they rallied again, and attacked our Scowerers with great Fury. The Fight was bloody and obstinate, and Victory seemed doubtful which Side to favour; but at last she declared for the Magistrate of the Night, who disarmed our Champions, and carried every Mother's Son of them to his Watch-house.

THE TRIAL OF MR COOKE,

MALT DISTILLER, AT STRATFORD,

FOR ADULTERY WITH MRS WALFORD,

WIFE OF MR WALFORD,

OF THE SAME PLACE;

BEFORE LORD KENYON,

AT WESTMINSTER HALL, JUNE, 1789.

THE plaintiff laid his damages at 10,000*l* – The declaration stated, that, at various times, and in different places therein mentioned, the defendant, with force and arms, assaulted Sophia, the wife of the plaintiff, and had carnal knowledge of her body.

Mr Parke having opened the pleadings, Mr Erskine addressed the Bench and Jury as follows:

I am counsel for Mr Walford, who brings this action against Mr Cooke, for one of the most aggravated injuries which one man can possibly offer to another. Mr Cooke, the defendant, has been engaged in trade, is in partnership with his father, and is a very opulent man. By living in the neighbourhood of Mr Walford, he became acquainted with him and his family. In the year 1781, Mr Walford was married to his wife (who is represented to me as a person of great beauty), and lived with her in the greatest harmony. I believe it will not be in the power of the defendant to disprove what I am now about to state; that Mr Walford lived in the most perfect happiness and harmony with his lady, and had by her, as he thought at least, a child, the comfort of which he is now entirely deprived of, and is reduced to a state which I am sure, gentlemen, will excite your commiseration. You will find that the conduct of Mr Cooke is mixed with everything that is improper; that it has been accompanied with fraud, with design, with deliberate and secret seduction, taking the opportunity of his situation, which he could not have had but by holding himself out, if not as the particular friend, yet as the acquaintance of Mr Walford, coming into his house and availing himself of Mr Walford's hospitality. But what makes this case in a moral view infinitely stronger, is that Mr Cooke, the defendant, is married, and to a woman equally beautiful with the wife of the plaintiff.

Mr Walford lived at Stratford; and on the 14th of February last came from his house, to London, on some business. On his return home he found the defendant at his house, in company with his wife and her aunt; it was a little before dinner. Mr Walford, as a man of polite manner, had no suspicion of the defendant, and therefore asked him to stay to dinner. Mr Cooke said he was very much obliged to him, and remained at dinner. The conversation turned on a masquerade that was to be at the Pantheon on the following Monday; the defendant said it would be pleasant to go. Mr Walford did not much approve of it; Mr Cooke still urged the pleasure of the scene; Mrs Walford was also extremely pressing that her husband should allow her to go. The husband, intending to accompany her, at last consented to this party, provided that she could find a lady to accompany her. The defendant, Mr Cooke, proposed a lady to accompany them. Mr Walford said, that neither he nor Mrs Walford was acquainted with that lady. So that Miss Porter, an acquaintance of Mr and Mrs Walford, was at last fixed upon to accompany them. They went to Mr Cooke's lodgings. Mr Cooke said it would be unnecessary to have a coach, and to keep servants very late, as a Mr Hall, who had been coachman to his father, would bring them a coach at any time; and this was agreed to. The husband had not the smallest suspicion on earth.

They went to the masquerade; and as in the course of such an amusement they must necessarily separate, they fixed on a particular place where they should meet every half hour. Mr Walford walked with Miss Porter under his arm, and the defendant, Mr Cooke, with Mrs Walford. From time to time Mrs Walford and Mr Cooke came to the place of rendezvous, and continued to meet one another every half hour until after supper, when Mrs Walford and Mr Cooke were not to be found. You may guess, gentlemen, the anxiety of Mr Walford, waiting a great length of time for his wife, with whom he had lived in the greatest harmony, though this man had wickedly and secretly seduced her before that time, and went to the masquerade to make her elope from her husband altogether. Mr Walford thinking his wife might be taken ill, and had retired, went to the defendant's lodgings; when he was told that they had been there, and left their masquerade dresses, and gone off in Mr Hall's coach, though they did not know where.

He then thought Mr Cooke had carried Mrs Walford home to his house at Stratford, which affording him momentary consolation, he went home; but, to his utter mortification, he was told they had not been there. He then went back to Mr Cooke's lodgings, but could hear no tidings of them; then to Mr Hall's, and was informed by one of his men, that he had driven them into a street near Soho-square, where they got out of the coach, and desired him to go away.

Gentlemen, you will hear from a Mr Stone, whom Mr Walford requested to go to Mr Cooke's, to have an interview with him, and know what had become of his lady, that Mr Cooke then acknowledged that he had carried Mrs Walford away from the masquerade; where they agreed to go for the purpose of an elopement; and that he could not bring her up to that step, but in a moment of gaiety and folly: and that during the time Mrs Walford had lived with her husband, he had secretly seduced her; and was the father of her child.

Gentlemen, I think it would only be wasting my lord's time and yours, to make any commentary on this case. When I remember to whom I am addressing myself, I am certain no such commentary is necessary.

I am not aware of any circumstances which can be alledged in mitigation of damages, and therefore I shall not anticipate them.

The marriage being proved, Miss Porter was examined by Mr Parke.

She said she was acquainted with Mr and Mrs Walford, and remembered her going to the masquerade, in consequence of an invitation, with them in February last. Mr Cooke, Mr and Mrs Walford, came to her at almost twelve o'clock at night; they went to the Pantheon in a coach. She did not remember any particular conversation between Mrs Walford and Mr Cooke in the coach. They were separated by the company, but met at a particular place. The witness took hold of Mr Walford's arm, and Mrs Walford took hold of Mr Cooke's. It was impossible for them not to separate; they met occasionally, she believed, once or twice at the place of rendezvous. They all supped together. They were again separated after supper, and she did not see Mrs Walford and Mr Cooke any more. They waited till

about five in the morning, and searched every part of the room to no purpose, and then went home with Mr Walford.

She also said, that Mrs Walford had a child, which might be near five years of age, and Mr Walford seemed to be very fond of it.

On her cross-examination she said, that on the night they were at the Pantheon, she did not observe any levity or misconduct in Mrs Walford's behaviour; nor any improper liberties on the part of Mr Cooke: and that the separation which took place at the masquerade, was nothing more than what arose from the necessity of the company.

Mr Thomas Stone, examined by Mr Erskine, said he saw this unhappy man (Mr Walford, the plaintiff,) the morning after this unlucky accident. Mr Walford appeared to the witness to be in the greatest state of distraction. He never saw a man more distressed. He had known him about seven, or eight years, and had visited him frequently. Mr Walford had likewise been very often at his house, and Mrs Stone and Mrs Walford, in point of intimacy, were like two sisters.

Mr and Mrs Walford, he said, were exceedingly happy, and very fond of each other. She was a very handsome woman, and her husband was fond of her to a degree of absurdity. This fondness was accompanied with all the attention that usually accompany it. He never observed any carelessness or neglect on Mr Walford's part. They had a child of about two years and a half old. Mr Walford was most attached to the child.

There was a report, he said, about three years ago, at Stratford, that an improper connexion subsisted between Mr Cooke and Mrs Walford, which the witness in confidence communicated to Mr Walford.

At the request of Mr Walford, Mr Stone went to Mr Cooke's lodgings the day after the masquerade. Mr Cooke was not at home; the witness left a note expressing a desire to see him. Mr Cooke called at the witness's house at nine o'clock on that night, and informed him that Mrs Walford was then in a coach in Fleet-street.

When Mr Walford called upon Mr Stone on the morning after the masquerade, he informed him that he, Mrs Walford and Mr Cooke, had been at the masquerade the over night; that he did not know what had become of his wife, but suspected that she had eloped with Mr Cooke, and begged him to call at Mr Cooke's lodgings to enquire after her, which he did, but, as has just been stated, did not find Mr Cooke at home. But, in consequence of his being informed that Mrs Walford was in a coach in Fleet-street, he accompanied Mr Cooke, and Mr Cooke went into the coach where Mrs Walford was.

Mrs Walford then told Mr Stone that Mr Cooke had desired her to relate to him what had passed between her and Mr Cooke. She accordingly told him that an improper intimacy had subsisted between her and Mr Cooke as far back as four or five years. That the child which she then had, was got on her by Mr Cooke; and that they had long intended to go off together, but were at a loss what they should do with the child.

Mr Cooke had applied to Mr Price, his attorney, to know whether they might, by law, take the child with them, and Mr Price advised him not to do it.

Here Mr Bearcroft, on the part of Mr Cooke, the defendant, submitted to Lord Kenyon, whether this was not the subject of a separate action, and which therefore could not be given in evidence upon this trial.

His Lordship said he conceived that this circumstance might legally be given in evidence, because it was not followed by any effect, as the child was never taken away from Mr Walford.

Mr Stone then stated to his Lordship and the Jury, that in this conversation between Mrs Walford and Mr Cooke, in the coach in Fleet-street, Mrs Walford told him, that she and Mr Cooke had fixed for going off on the Friday se'nnight before, but that Mr Cooke having been necessarily detained on account of some partnership business, that project had been laid aside.

The witness said, that he then asked Mr Cooke whether he went to the masquerade for the purpose of carrying Mrs Walford off; to which he answered, that he did not intend then to have carried her off. Mr Cooke further told the witness, that they had had an infinite deal of difficulty in preventing Mr Walford from knowing this business; but that they had prevented him. He wished it could have been accomplished in a more private manner; but as it had happened it was now as well. He wished to go to France; but Mrs Walford objected to it.

Being then asked what he meant to do? Mr Cooke said, that

when a man had debauched a woman, it was his duty to protect her; and that that was his situation with Mrs Walford.

Mr Stone then proposed taking Mrs Walford home to his house, to try to rescue her from Mr Cooke, which was at first strongly opposed by both of them, for fear of an interview with Mr Walford; however, after two hours conversation, and Mr Stone's giving Mrs Walford his honour that her husband should not see her, she consented, and accordingly went to his house. He had afterwards another interview with Mr Cooke, and in consequence of a conversation, Mr Cooke came again to his house, and said that he would have no more to do with Mrs Walford; but at the same time promised that, if she would return to him, he would certainly protect her.

Mrs Walford remained at Mr Stone's two days, and then returned to Mr Cooke.

Mr Stone said, that Mr Cooke was a married man,* and is a man of property.

Mr Stone, it seems, as before hinted, had heard a report, three years ago, of an improper connexion between Mr Cooke and Mrs Walford, and informed Mr Walford of this unpleasant circumstance, who asked his advice what he should do.

By Mr Walford's desire he then went to Mr Cooke to enquire about the truth of this report. Mr Cooke assured him, in the most solemn manner, that it was entirely without foundation. But being asked whether some letters had not passed between him and Mrs Walford, which had found their way into the hands of his (Mr Cooke's) father, Mr Cooke immediately referred him to his father for the truth of what he asserted: he also requested Mr Stone to communicate this information to Mr Walford not to drop his intimacy with Mr Cooke on account of this report.

The child was born at the time Mr Cooke made this solemn declaration of his innocence of any criminal intimacy with Mrs Walford. Mr Stone, however, observed that he was extremely surprised at the conversation that passed in the hackey-coach in Fleet-street, when he compared it with the solemn declaration made by Mr Cooke three years before.

* Mrs Cooke, we understand, entertains notions of gallantry of equal liveliness with those of her husband, she having eloped with another person. She is a very beautiful woman.

The letters before-mentioned were supposed to have passed between Mr Cooke and Mrs Walford when Mrs Walford lay-in.

Mr Stone, cross-examined by Mr Fielding, said, that among other reasons why he thought the report of a criminal connexion three years ago, between Mrs Walford and Mr Cooke, was unfounded, was, that he had heard that Mrs Walford and Mr Cooke had been seen together in Epping Forest, at a time when, to his certain knowledge, Mrs Walford was ill at his house in Thames-street, and had been for four days confined to her bed.

Mrs Walford, he said, had been three or four months at a time at his house; he then had a house at Hampstead; and Mrs Stone was at home during part of the time that Mrs Walford was there.

During the time that Mrs Walford was at his house, Mr Walford was not constantly with her; he came to town occasionally about his business. Mrs Walford was there sometimes in the absence both of her husband and of Mrs Stone; but at that time a gentleman and two ladies were at his house.

The witness also observed that he never was, in an innocent gambol, locked up in a bed-chamber in his house with Mrs Walford.

Lord Kenyon here informed him, that he was not bound to answer any question that tended to criminate himself, and that he might answer such questions or not, as he pleased.

The witness said, that he had no objection whatever to answer every question that was put to him.

He then further declared, that he was never locked up in a bed-chamber with Mrs Walford; but he recollected, that once, when he and Mrs Walford were in a room together, the maid-servant came to the door, he desired her to stop a little, at that time Mrs Stone, and seven or eight ladies, were in the next room drinking tea.

The reason why he did not open the door immediately to the maid-servant, was, that there was *some china* at the back of the door, and therefore he desired her to stop until it *was removed*.

This servant-girl, he added, came to him about a fortnight ago, informing him that she was subpoenaed on this cause, and asked him what she was called upon to prove? He did not detain her a minute at the door; and that there were several telescopes and other curiosities in this room, which Mrs Walford and himself were viewing, when the maid-servant came to the door: that Mrs Walford frequently slept in his house, when her husband was not there; that Mr Walford came out every other night; and that he, the witness, had an opportunity of seeing Mr Walford's treatment of his wife, which was always very proper.

Mr Fielding then proceeding to ask the witness questions, Mr Erskine objected to them, as tending to crimination.

Mr Bearcroft said, he, once for all, wished to submit to the court, whether the regular practice was not to put the questions? There was some questions which might be put; but it depended on the witness, whether he should answer them or not.

Mr Erskine observed, that it had been given in evidence that this lady (Mrs Walford) and Mrs Stone were intimate as sisters; that the door was not shut on account of any gallantry, nor any criminal connexion between Mrs Walford and Mr Stone.

Arol Smith, next called on the part of the plaintiff, said he had known the parties nearly six years. That they had visited him; that he had always received Mrs Walford as a modest decent woman, and never observed any thing to the contrary, and that her husband always appeared to be a very tender and affectionate husband, and that that sort of happiness always subsisted between them, which makes matrimony truly desirable.

William Savage was then examined, and gave an evidence exactly of the same tendency. He had known the parties upwards of twenty years.

A Mr Morrison followed the same tract, and added, that he was very intimate with them for about a year and a half; that the behaviour of Mrs Walford afforded no reasonable cause of suspicion, otherwise he should not have visited her and Mr Walford, nor introduced his sisters to them.

Mr Slater, the last witness examined on behalf of the plaintiff, praised Mr Walford's conduct as the most exemplary for tenderness and affection; and added, that his conduct towards the child had always been very affectionate.

DEFENCE

Mr Bearcroft now addressed the Judge and the Jury in the following manner:

I hope you will pardon my stepping out,* because it might have saved you a great deal of trouble. It so happens, however, that it will not have that advantage. And I am now to address you on the part of the defendant.

I confess I feel myself now standing in an aukward situation. If I did not, I should have no pretensions to any feeling, or to any discretion.

It has ever been my idea that the best way of doing service to my clients, when I stand before such a judge and such a jury as I now do, is to treat things with a little regard to truth and decency.

You may rest assured I do not get up, as Mr Erskine seemed to insinuate, to insult the plaintiff, or any thing like it; if I did, it would have, and ought to have, this effect – extremely to aggravate the damages in a case of this kind.

Gentlemen, if I had been permitted to exercise my own judgment in this case, I should not have troubled you with any evidence on the part of the defendant; but should have left the matter to my lord's judgment and your own.

But certain it is, when counsel have stated their opinion to their clients, and have put a peremptory question, whether witnesses should be called or not, it is their duty, no doubt, to conform to the inclinations of their clients.

I stand in a situation in which I am to produce witnesses on the part of the defendant; a situation which I have most frequently had occasion to lament. And I protest that I cannot help making this general observation; and for the truth of it I appeal to his lordship, and to every gentleman wearing a gown, if the situation of counsel for a defendant is not such universally, as it is hardly a mode of trial that does justice to the defendant. A counsel for the plaintiff may say some things, or not, just as he find necessary or convenient; he has all his witnesses to prove his case, and knows what they will say. The defendant has to call witnesses, uncertain what they will say, and without knowing what will be the effect of their testimony. There is not equal justice in this mode of trial; for the counsel for the plaintiff having gone through his evidence, having heard the evidence for the defendant, after the defendant's mouth is shut

* Before Mr Bearcroft addressed the jury, he went out of court to consult on this business with the defendant's father.

165

in point of observation, has an opportunity of making observations on that evidence in his own way. This, in the present case, is the fortunate situation of my learned friend, who possesses powers equal to those of any man.

I admit that, by the testimony which the Plaintiff has given, he has entitled himself to a verdict. I will go a little further; I will admit that, from the evidence which the plaintiff has given, he has made out a case which certainly does call for some damages.

My client was a young man at that moment, who appears to have put himself in a situation by which the plaintiff has suffered materially, and the plaintiff has a right to call upon him for damages.

Mr Cooke is a young man, the son, among others, of a gentleman in a considerable situation in trade. Notwithstanding the case produced on the part of the plaintiff, if I can produce, on the part of the defendant, witnesses who will shew you that this lady, so far from having been debauched by the defendant, was what she is now proved to be; if I prove that the husband was much in fault; that he was in that situation and deserved that character; all these will be very material circumstances in that situation. If I prove that they lived ill together; if I prove that the conduct of the husband has been vicious in the extreme, even with his own wife; if I prove these things to your satisfaction, it will take away all idea of serious damages; for then the case would turn out to be this – that the plaintiff deserves all that he has suffered.

Whether this case exists or not, neither you nor I can tell, until the witnesses are called; it is my duty, therefore, to call them without further preface or statement, such as will lay the whole case before you, upon which you will exercise your judgments, and will give such damages as the substantial justice of it requires.

EVIDENCE FOR THE DEFENDANT

James Eyre said, that he had been long acquainted with Mr and Mrs Walford; and that Mr Walford behaved very well to his wife, so far as ever he saw.

At the same time, he confessed, Mr Walford might have taken

some little liberties with his wife before the witness, which another man, perhaps, might not have done.

He was then a single man, but Mr Walford, he said, had often brought his wife to his house to ride one of the witness's horses.

Mrs Walford was extremely fond of *riding*; she and Mr Eyre used frequently to ride out together by themselves; they had often, likewise, gone to the *play* by themselves; and all with the knowledge, privity, and consent of Mr Walford.

The witness shrewdly observed, being now married, that he should not take his wife to any single man's house to ride out with him.

He further said, he had been at their house many evenings, when Mr Walford, sitting before the fire, himself on one side and Mrs Walford on the other, Mr Walford used to kick up Mrs Walford's toes, which threw up her petticoats, so that the witness could see her knees.

Mr Walford would then say to the witness, D—n me, Jem, she has got a pretty leg! – Still he did not immediately recollect any indecent conduct on Mrs Walford's part.

Mr and Mrs Walford were sometimes at the witness's house, and had often breakfasted, dined, and supped together.

James Eyre, the witness, had many times breakfasted, dined, and supped with Mrs Walford by herself, in her bed-chamber – but this happened when she was ill for a week, or ten days, at his house, and when Mr Walford came and slept there.

On his cross-examination he said, that he had been in partnership with Mr Walford, and that an intimacy and friendship subsisted between them – the plaintiff confided in him as a man of integrity and honour; and that when he so breakfasted, dined, and supped with Mrs Walford by herself, he did not think he was acting with indelicacy; adding, that Mr Walford was very fond of his wife.

Mr Sayer said, the defendant's father was a gentleman of property; but being asked whether he was not worth one hundred thousand pounds? he submitted it to the court, whether he was bound to answer this question? – Lord Kenyon said, he might answer it if he pleased, but he was obliged to answer no question which tended to expose the situation of their house, or the state of their affairs.

The witness said, that the defendant was in partnership with his father, who is a malt distiller; and that his capital was advanced by the father, who owned every shilling of it; and that he, the defendant, was the only child.

Mr Mingay asked if a malt-distiller was not a very profitable business? – To which the witness replied, That they sometimes got money, and sometimes lost money; it was not like the profession of gentlemen at the bar! To this Mr Mingay answered, That malt-distillers could distil many things which counsel at the bar could not!

Mr Erskine then replied to Mr Bearcroft.

May it please your Lordship, and you, Gentlemen of the Jury:

I do not remember one case like this in all my experience at the bar. As my learned friend (Mr Bearcroft) knew every thing he was to prove was a false calumny; as he knew from his instructions it was false, and from the witnesses, that it could not be true, his own judgment was against producing evidence, which, if he could have produced, would have turned the scale in his favour.

Why hope to get that from a witness which does not exist in point of fact?

Is there any evidence to prove, that Mr Walford did not watch over the beauty of his wife, or that he suffered her to behave with levity; or, like too many husbands, permit her to go to scenes of vice and folly without any attendant; a practice which disgraces this metropolis? This husband only goes to a masquerade, and all of a sudden finds himself deprived of his wife. Yet his opponents produce a gentleman, who, at the time he was in partnership with Mr Walford, being in a state of distress, and having no house in town, asks his friends to furnish his wife with an apartment; I say, they produce this gentleman to tell you, that he breakfasted, dined, and supped with Mrs Walford. Was there any thing improper or indecent in this? This gentleman had this opportunity as a friend; so that you have a man who seems to be an example to husbands, and whose conduct has been the most tender and affectionate towards his wife.

The plaintiff only asks a satisfaction at your hands for this very serious injury which he has sustained; an adequate compensation you cannot make him. At the same time, gentlemen, your duty to yourselves, as well as to the public at large, requires that you should give him special and most exemplary damages.

To Mr Erskine's question, whether there was any thing improper or indecent in Mr Walford's partner supping, &c. with his wife, it may be answered in the affirmative, unless the testimony of Mr Eyre, relative to the *leg-scene*, be invalidated – If it had not been thought that this gentleman feasted his eyes as well as his appetite, there could have been no occasion for the exclamation, 'D——m me, Jem, she has got a pretty leg!'

Lord Kenyon's Address to the Jury

Gentlemen of the Jury,

Since I have had the honour of sitting in this place, I have much too often had occasion to state to juries my sense of injuries of this kind. When I say, that it is almost the highest injury that man can receive from man, I believe I only meet the feelings of honourable and decent men.

That the injury has been committed, is proved beyond all contradiction. That the relation of husband and wife subsisted between Mr and Mrs Walford has likewise been proved by the first witness who has given his evidence in this cause.

That Mr Cooke has had that criminal intercourse with Mrs Walford which this declaration imputes to him, is admitted in a conversation held in his presence, and detailed by Mrs Walford at his request, and therefore your verdict must be for the plaintiff.

But there is one circumstance, namely, the damages; on which I beg leave to say a few words: – Offences of this kind admit of infinite gradations. They are either criminal in the highest degree, or circumstances may mix with them, which, in some degree, may reduce the criminality, or may even go in a great measure to take away the whole offence, so far as the offence is concerned.

Where the husband is privy to the seduction of his wife, and where the injury is owing to his own misconduct, though the person who offends is not, in the eye of God, delivered from his crime, yet the husband has not a right to expect large damages from a jury.

But if the offence, as in this instance, has been committed without the knowledge of the husband, after he had lived on terms of uninterrupted happiness with his wife, if the husband has deserved to receive a return of affection from her, because he had unremittingly bestowed affection upon her; if, during their cohabitation together, children are born, which are supposed to be the fruit of their marriage, though these children are found not to be his, yet they reap all the legal rights of legitimate children, and no power on earth, but the legislature, can alter this.

Children born in this situation inherit rights, of which the father cannot disinherit them. This child, in the eye of the law, must be regarded as the father's.

This offence may be further aggravated, if the adulterer obtained access to the wife by gaining the confidence of her husband; if he has visited the husband as his friend, and the friend of his family. In the unguarded moment when the husband consented to go to the masquerade, he thought he took a person with him who would protect his wife; and in order that all decorum might be preserved, another lady, to whose character no blame has been imputed, went along with them.

I protest, it appears to me, that every thing was done on the part of the husband, which decorum, decency, affection, and attention to his wife required: so that the plaintiff seems to have been extremely circumspect in almost every circumstance of his conduct; yet I admit, I think, that a cautious person, a very guarded man, when he had heard there was a suspicion that this defendant had a criminal intercourse with his wife, would not have selected him to go to the masquerade, although he had a solemn protestation to the satisfaction of his friend, that this report was unfounded. This is the only circumstance which imputes want of circumspection to the plaintiff; this might fall, however, on a very prudent man: no man is prudent every moment of his life.

It is clear from the evidence, that Mr and Mrs Walford lived in the greatest happiness and harmony, and that this affection for his wife was unremitting.

There is one circumstance more, and that is, the situation in life in which the defendant is; and here it was very properly observed by the counsel for the plaintiff, that although a man is poor, and unable to pay, he is not to go free: for when a man, in a case like this, cannot pay by his purse, he must pay by his person. And God forbid, that a man who has had originally no fortune, or who has dissipated it, should be allowed to commit this offence, and should be permitted with impunity to break the peace of families.

Gentlemen, a great deal is due from you to this plaintiff; and something is likewise due to the public at large. It is of the greatest importance to the public, that every member of the community should observe the rules of morality and religion.

To you, therefore, is committed the protection of the peace of families; and if small damages were to be given in this case, unless you could mould new men, and give them better minds than many now possess, you would be reading a lesson to them, that they might indulge their appetites at pleasure.

The plaintiff is a man of honour, character, and decorum you will give him what damages you think proper; none, however great, can make reparation for the wounded peace of his mind.

The jury having deliberated about half an hour, brought in a verdict for the plaintiff, of Three Thousand Five Hundred Pounds!

There has been so much morality in the course of this trial, through the channel of the counsels' speeches, and the judge's charge, that anything more of that kind would be superfluous. However, to simple readers, and those unacquainted with the law, the invalidated part of Mr Eyre's evidence, relative to Mr Walford's kicking up of Mrs Walford's petticoats, is a part that, we are persuaded, must still remain a mystery!

AMUSEMENTS
In HIGH LIFE;
OR,

Conjugal Infidelities in 1786.

IN A
Series of CONFIDENTIAL LETTERS,
BETWEEN

LADIES who have diftinguifhed themfelves
by the Multiplicity and Singularity

OF THEIR

AMOURS.

Fidelity in Wives is all a Joke,
Whilft there's a Coffin, Shrubb'ry, or an Oak.

A NON.

LONDON:
Printed for G. LISTER, No. 46, OLD BAILEY.
MDCCLXXXVI.

Caroline to Eliza

In my fifteenth year I found myself alive to those sensations which nature and flattery inspire at that age; my person was agreeable, and I knew it. Variety, that prevalent ingredient in our composition, actuated me to extend the train of my admirers. In coquettry I soon became an adept. But amongst the number over whom I had the power of attraction, the attentions of two were particular to me. Mr Bevil, and Will Ramble, two characters, opposites in every thing; the manners of the one were gentle, sedate, and tender, those of the other were dissipated and full of vivacity; a continual circle of pleasures, in which I often participated, were the employment of his life: his wandering fancy evinced a difficulty of fixing his heart, for which prize there were many rivals; emulation sets a value upon a man destitute of all intrinsic worth. This he perceived and availed himself of it. My pride would not suffer me to be outdone. I dressed at him; some particular attentions on his side, assured me the appearance of success. I triumphed in my own breast at the conquest; he improved in his partiality to me; and, from the opinion my folly entertained of his taste, I attributed the decision in my favour to my own merit, and then began to assume that authority which love gives us over our slaves. I affected to dally with Mr Bevil; this always awoke his jealousy; Bevil, who was not disagreeable to me, and in whom I could easily trace the appearances of a genuine passion, put on an air of chearfulness, at which he called my condescension; his gentle sensibility became the object of Ramble's raillery, which he had not effrontery to withstand. I joined in the laugh at his expence: a party of pleasure of Ramble's proposing always drew me away from the sedate conversation of Bevil, who was left to repine alone at the hardships of his situation.

One evening that worthy man chanced to meet me alone at home, in the absence of my mother, who countenanced his addresses. With every mark of genuine respect, he addressed me on the subject of his passion; he assured me, that it was with difficulty he could assume a topic in which his happiness was so deeply interested; the passion, continued he, your merit has inspired me with, is but too apparent not to be perceived. I flatter myself, that I may have some degree of share in your esteem, and that your heart is not totally unconcerned about a man, who has no other view that your honour and happiness in conjunction with his own. If a term more tender than that of love, could be found to express my sentiments, even that would not do justice to my feelings; you are the arbitress of my happiness, and I only entreat an answer, as candid as my request is sincere – Here he pressed my hand, while his voice faultered. I blushed, but, collecting myself, charged him with raillery, and said such language was the common artifice of his sex. He disavowed the justice of the charge, and, kneeling, pressed me to an explanation. The fervor and agitation of his manner excited in me a fit of laughter. I compared him to one of the sanctified, who quake on the emotions of the spirit, and recommended him to mount the rostrum at some tabernacle, where his manner might captivate one of the holy sisterhood, who groan in the flesh as well as the spirit. I wished for Ramble's presence, who was an excellent proficient in caricature; assuring him that the present position was a happy attitude for ridicule.

Stung to the heart, he rose up, and going to the door, he assured me that the interest he had in my happiness would never permit him to intrude again; and that he would leave the field to his happy rival. He bowed respectfully, retired, and kept his word faithfully; for he avoided my company, from that day forward, as much as possible. His conduct gave me some uneasiness for a while, but assuming my pride, I affected in myself to despise a man who did not think me worth a second repulse. I then sported my influence over Ramble, as a retaliation on Bevil.

Ramble, who imputed the discontinuance of Bevil's addresses to the decisive preference he had in my eyes, redoubled his assiduities, which now had found the sure road to my heart. My mother's inclinations against the success of a man of such noted levity, gave cause to many clandestine assignations between us, at each of which he appeared in raptures. A profession of mutual love took off restraint from our sentiments; I avowed my partiality for him, without blushing. He was ruler of my heart and conduct; he was not ignorant of his influence, and I became miserable in his absence. My mother, from my unusual pensiveness and solitude, was alarmed for the state of my health; my agonies were increased from an absence of above a week, of my lover, from the park, the place where we casually met; she determined on taking lodgings at Kensington for the benefit of the air, on my account, which she instantly put into execution. I obeyed reluctantly, and was constrained to the humiliating means of sending Ramble an anonymous account of our retreat; not considering that I run the hazard of courting the company of a man, in whom perhaps was effaced every impression of regard that I thought it his duty to entertain for me.

But all prudence yielded to the irresistible tyranny of love. He replied, apologized for his absence, and took lodgings near us. It was that month when revived nature was decorated in her glittering garb, May, wafted on the wings of fragrant zephyrs, had all happiness complete to me when he appeared. Our interviews were stolen; maternal prudence had but little weight in the scale against a passion so fervent and entire as mine; when Ramble made no assignation, I undertook the task without reluctance to see him.

News came to my mother that her sister, who lived at Windsor, had met with a violent hurt by the over-turning of her carriage. She flew on the wings of impatience to see her: I was left at home, sole mistress of my conduct and our apartments; our servants I permitted to go to town, the people of the house were gone out to spend Whitsun Monday. Ramble, who watched my mother's conduct, was acquainted with her departure; he solicited to spend the evening at our lodgings; my easy heart yielded to his request; he came; we were alone: his impassioned transports urged me to propose the connubial bond as a privilege to his liberties. He vowed, with rapture, that it was his only desire, and, if practicable, to put it into immediate execution. But how to effect it, during the small interval of time in which my mother would be absent, and reap the joys of a golden opportunity which might not offer again, was an objection of the last importance. Did I doubt his honour, he asked me, with a tender languor; he did appear in my eyes to be that worthless wretch, who deserved mistrust; did he sacrifice all pretensions to the rest of my sex for me only, to stand suspected as unworthy my confidence? Surely he did not centre all his happiness in one object to rob her of her's? He conjured heaven and

earth to witness the sincerity of his intentions, and condemned himself to punishment, ten-fold severer than any human ingenuity could devise, were he capable of harbouring a thought inconsistent with the most tender and lasting affection. – I was silent, and gave vent to my swoln heart with a flood of tears. He kissed them off my cheeks. Relieved by these, my inward tumults subsided, reason began to resume her sway. I then strove to argue with him; his artifice confuted the objections of my willing mind. I sunk into his arms upon the sopha; nature ruled the helm within me; the tide of love rolled impetuous through my veins, and broke down the barriers of guiding reason, and all my fortitude ended in proving me – a woman.

The precious jewel we part from with such anxiety, and when lost regret so bitterly, was now gone from me beyond the power of recal. I pressed the robber of it to my bosom, I measured my extacies by the fleeting minutes, and wished to arrest their anxious speed. Night approaching, reminded us of the hour of separation: he stayed late, and from the improbability of my mother's return, he urged me to suffer him to pass the night with me; I willingly complied, after arranging matters so as render his escape easy through the garden in case of necessity. Delight and rapture occupied the space till the ill-natured approach of the sun-beams warned us of separating.

I conveyed him out with safety, retired to my solitary pillow, and gave myself up to the arms of a delicious slumber.

Adieu my dear Eliza. Pity me, pity your sympathizing
CAROLINE

Eliza to Caroline

Your reasons, dear Caroline, convince me that I acted right, and that in following the bent of my inclinations, I only did justice to the wretch who robbed me of my happiness, and debarred me from the fair possession of the choice of my heart. I made reprisals, as far as circumstances would allow. Oh! that I could but hear that you had spirit enough to despise the unworthy being, on whom you bestowed your affections. That you should remain long, after such an instance of ingratitude, a victim to a passion for so base a male prostitute, is inconsistent with that spirit I know you to possess: wound up to the height of happiness, and so speedily precipitated from its summit to the lowest pit of despair! The alternative was misery. What must you not have felt, as sufferer, when the very recital gives me such inexpressible anguish? I knew the person whose wealth bribed your undoer; a humpback, distorted features, and two knees at perpetual war, the underprops of a waddling rump, gave her the appearance of a caricature on human nature; a temper of mind, as ill-disposed as her body was deformed, frightened mankind from her presence. Can you envy Ramble such an acqustion, and after his perfidy to acquire it? I would, in your place, unconcernedly leave him an undisturbed possession. Write to me then, my dear friend, the result. You had, I am sure, a happy riddance of such a companion for life.

My assignations with Jemmy Fairfield, were many and agreeable; he was of a discreet and circumspect turn of mind; his manners were not vitiated with the fopperies and dissipation of a coxcomb: he was a thinking person, and added a fairness of character to a sound constitution. Five weeks brought about the power of motion in my husband; he made an attempt to storm that fort, where he thought man never entered before. Though willing to yield like a prudent commander, I defended the garrison for a time, and at length capitulated; the conqueror made his entry, explored the works, and deposited the dearest treasure of which he was master, in the body of the citadel. He groaned with extacy, I returned like caresses. There is, my dear, the foundation stone laid for a son. But that business was done to his hand. Too well I knew the difference of capacities between that masculine and sappy sprout, which was able to effect the purpose, and that tendinous production of exhausted membrane, which lolled out from between the skin and bone of a withered carcase. A violent fit of coughing had like to have strangled him; with much ado he expectorated the tough phlegm from his breast. I wiped his mouth, as soon as he was at ease. – I cuddled him in my arms to sleep.

The anxiety I had for a premature delivery, was now at an end: my dotard, confident of his own ability, was fully persuaded that his effort was successful. I flattered his vanity by a silent assent. I conformed my conduct to his pleasure in every thing, and received in return, all the fondness and indulgence of impotence. My restraint grew less daily. Jemmy had a false key to our garden door, on the rear of the house, which led to a retired summer-house that I fitted up and converted into a library, and hung the inside of the windows with Venetian blinds, with a strict charge not to suffer them to be raised up. He came there secretly every day. The floor was covered with a carpet, lined and quilted with wool between the divisions; the underpart of a book-case, where a man could sit at ease, was left vacant. Thither he crept for concealment on his entry, as he was likewise furnished with a key to open the lock: a bolt within secured him, till my approach released him from his prison, to enfold him in my arms. One caution was not neglected, for lest a busy eye should perceive his entrance without the garden door, he had the coat and the hat of a peasant, concealed at a distance from the house, which he put on to elude the eye of observation. I undertook to compose a poem in praise of wisdom, and the happiness of a matrimonial engagement with a faithful turtle, whose sage experience and wisdom were the true guardians of honour and happiness in a virtuous wife; and contrasted the dangers to which a woman's virtue is exposed, when a dissipated and false coxcomb falls to her lot; whose example and conduct are inducements to retaliate. I addressed it to my husband; he was delighted with the thought, and extolled the language, which he said was worthy so well-chosen a subject. I choose the solitary retirement of the summer-house for my study, he often came to hear me recite those passages which pleased his taste, and sometimes plagued me with his company for an hour, to my no small mortification for the suffering of my Jemmy.

The following lines he pitched upon out of the poem, to hang under my picture.

> Oh! hap'ly rescued from the storms of life,
> In honour's harbour lives the wise man's wife;
> The age and prudence of her pilot proves
> The firmest anchor to secure their loves;
> Where beauty yielding to affection's sway,
> Through duty's paths, she bends her willing way;
> There freed from all that can give rude alarms,
> She takes her refuge in her husband's arms.

Be so good, my dear Caroline, to substitute *youth* for *age* in the third line, and *lover* in the eighth to *husband*, and read it again. Adieu, my dear; cease that melancholy account, and tell me what steps your own spirit rescued you from the delirium of that situation the faithless Ramble seduced you into. Arouse yourself; and turn to a more pleasing topic; and since life has bitterness enough that is inevitable, let us crop the flowers we can, and participate your joys to your

ELIZA

Caroline to Eliza

The complicated piece of aukwardness, and ignorance, to whom I vowed obedience, was the next difficulty I had to surmount; but how to do it, and preserve the name of affection to a man for whom I apparently made so great a sacrifice, required all my address. Under the masque of reforming him, I joined in the ridicule of such company as we kept, his rooted vulgarities were not to be removed. In endeavouring to teach him to play cards, if their course was not to his wishes, he scattered them upon the table, which he often overturned to divert himself; he put his hands frequently into the bosoms of young ladies, and, when reprimanded by my mother, he accused her with jealousy; because such an old *hunks* as she was not worth it, she envied the pleasure, he said, of those who were. When he wanted to retire from company, or was sleepy, his general address to me was, 'Come Lina, let us take our a———e in our hands and go pig it together, I'se sleepy, and I'll be damned if I stay for the king – come along girl.' – Such treatment determined me to be rid of him at any rate.

The attention paid me, by several smart young fellows, was a relief from his brutality, and amongst the number was one of those athletic adventurers from Hibernia, who imports more wit than money into our country. I gave him preference in the eyes of my husband, whose jealousy was excited; my view so far succeeded, I encouraged Mr O'Carrol's addresses, and insinuated that the life of my husband was an impediment to that happiness I had no objection to with him. He over-whelmed me with his fawning absurdity, but he had a fund of good nature. As soon as he understood what was the obstacle between him and my consent, he undertook to quarrel with my husband, and so give cause to a genteel mode of murder. He trod upon my husband's toes, three or four times, who at last resented it, by

offering to box him. 'Any weapon you please, honey,' says the Hibernian, 'from our own knuckle-bones, to a twenty-four pounder; as you never was a gentleman I will condescend to fight you at your own *weapons*, the first. Or what do you think of a case of blunderbusses, with sluggs, in a saw-pit? You will have more chance; for if you go to fisty work, you will have but little, as I'll make you dance to the tune of, Shela na gigg, on one of my hands, and with the other I will whip you like a top.' 'By Heaven man, I'll have nothing to do with you,' says my lord and master, 'but swear the peace against you.' He kept his word, and my champion was obliged to give security for his good behaviour; which being effected, the poor fellow was detained by a sheriff's officer at the suit of a tradesman, and obliged to go to a lock-up house.

The situation of my champion suggested to me an idea of sending his antagonist for company to him; the allowance my husband had was trifling, and he wholly depended on my mother for that. His vanity in cloaths was the only pardonable foible he had; he was indebted 60*l*, to his taylor, who made several applications in vain for his money. My mother protested against allowing him any more than she promised him. I took care to inform the taylor, at second hand, that nothing but compulsion could recover his money. The plan succeeded, and my deary was called out from breakfast, to an officer who conveyed him to a place of security. The enormous expence of living in a lock-up house, being too great for his income, and no resource coming from home, he was constrained to take up his residence on the south of London, under the care of Lord Mansfield. Detainers were lodged against him for other debts, which put the recovery of his liberty beyond hopes.

I now had my full swing, and gratitude obliged me to consider if I could serve the poor Irishman, whose debt and costs amounted only to 13*l*. I sent him a 20*l* bank note, he liberated himself. The effusions of thanks the poor fellow made to me, evinced that he was not deficient in sensibility; he continued to pay his attention to me, as the means of his delivery were known to him and me only; his perseverance in endeavouring to please me, got the better of my prejudice against his absurdities, so far as that he at last insinuated himself into my arms.

He won my esteem, and I now experienced all the enjoyments

which manly power can impart. We often passed whole nights together, when I was absent from home, under pretence of being with my husband. It was astonishing, my dear, what vigour animated this man; though when we met, he was always in a state of intoxication. The frequency and vigour of his attacks so weakened me, that my back and loins ached violently, my stomach could not retain any thing, my eyes swam in languor, my memory was impaired; the enjoyment of pleasure from such powers did not however affect my heart, the pleasure of sensation was all my object.

I saw and enjoyed company without reserve. I could now make advances to young fellows disencumbered of that restraint a girl must submit to. Why should I disavow that I loved flattery? the assiduities of my gallant were not equal to satisfy the appetite that passion inspired me with. The lesson I received from Ramble's perfidy, disposed me to sport with the feelings of all his sex. My gallant was the creature of my own pleasures. I received him on those terms only; and as he filled his post with such entire satisfaction, I resolved to continue him till he deserved my disgust. It was evident on both sides, our passion was not of that refined nature, which would produce regret on a separation. Sometimes three or four days elapsed without an interview, which encreased the stock to be expended in pleasure at our meeting. The prelude of sentiment was but short to the exercise of sensation; after which we parted mutually satisfied, making a future appointment. The interval I employed in a round of such pleasures as offered, as much at my ease as if nothing had happened.

Adieu, Eliza; continue the sequel of your journey, the party must have every inducement you could desire, when Cupid's disciple held the reins.

Your's, my dear,
CAROLINE

HARRIS's LIST

OF

COVENT-GARDEN LADIES:

OR,

MAN OF PLEASURE's

KALENDER,

For the YEAR, 1788.

CONTAINING

The Histories and some curious Anecdotes of the most celebrated Ladies now on the Town, or in keeping, and also many of their Keepers.

LONDON:

Printed for H. RANGER, (formerly at No. 23, *Fleet-Street,*) at No. 9, *Little Bridges-Street,* near *Drury-Lane Play-House*

Where may be had,

The separate LISTS of many preceding Years

Miss H——ll——nd, No 2, York Street, Queen-Anne-street.

> *No time shall pass without that dear delight,*
> *I'll talk of love all day, and act it all the night;*
> *Pleasure and I as to one goal design'd,*
> *Will run with equal pace, while sorrow lays behind.*

Those who choose to sail to the island of love in a *first rate* ship, or to enclose an armful of delight, must be pleased with this lady; who, tho' only seventeen and short, is very fat and corpulent; yet, notwithstanding, she is a fine piece of frailty; her face is handsome, and her *nut brown locks*, which are placed *above* and below, promise a luscious treat to the voluptuary. Her temper is agreeable and pleasing, and she is so far from being mercenary, that a single guinea is the boundage of her wish.

Miss B——rn, No 18, Old Compton Street, Soho.

> *Close in the arms she languishingly lies,*
> *With dying looks, short breath, and wishing eyes.*

This accomplished nymph has just attained her eighteenth year, and fraught with every perfection, enters a volunteer in the field of Venus. She plays on the piano forte, sings, dances, and is mistress of every *Manœuvre* in the amorous contest that can enhance the coming pleasure; is of the middle stature, fine auburn hair, dark eyes, and very inviting countenance, which ever seems to beam delight and love. In bed she is all the heart can wish, or eye admire, every limb is symmetry, every action under cover truly amorous; her price is two pounds two.

Miss J——ns——n, No 17, Goodge street, Charlotte street.

> *And all these joys insatiably to prove,*
> *With which rich beauty feasts the glutton love.*

The raven coloured tresses of Miss J——ns——n are pleasing, and are characteristics of strength and ability in the wars of Venus. Indeed this fair one is not afraid of work, but will undergo a great deal of labour in the action; she sings, dances, will drink a chearful glass, and is a good companion. She has such a noble elasticity in her loins, that she can cast her lover to a pleasing height, and receive him again with the utmost dexterity. Her price is one pound one, and for her person and amorous qualifications she is well worth the money.

Miss L—v—r, No 17, Ogle street, Queen Ann-street East.

> *She darted from her eyes a side long glance*
> *Just as she spoke, and, like her words, it flew,*
> *Seem'd not to beg, what yet she bid to do.*

This young nymph of fifteen is short, of a dark complexion, and inclinable to be lusty; she does not rely on *chamber practice* only, for she takes her evening excursions to seek for *clients*, who may put their case to her either in a tavern or her own apartments; her fee is from a crown to half a guinea, and she strives to earn her money by seeming to be agreeable; however, she may please some, and as we have only known her about four months she cannot have lost her *appetite*, but seems particularly fond of the sport.

Miss H—rd—y, No 45, Newman street.

> *Her look serene does purest softness wear,*
> *Her face exclaims her fairest of the fair.*

This lady borrows her names from her late keeper, who is now gone to the India's, and left her to seek support on the wide common of independence; she is now just arrived at the zenith of perfection, devoid of art and manners, as yet untutor'd by fashion, her charms have for heir zest every addition youth and simplicity can add. She has beauty without pride, elegance without affectation, and innocence without dissimulation; and not knowing how long this train of perfections will last, we would advise our reader to make hay whilst the sun shines.

Miss Br—wn, No 8, Castle-street, Newman-street.

> *Her every glance, like Jove's vindictive flame,*
> *Shoot thro' the veins, and kindle all the frame.*

A peculiar elegance in make and taste in dressing distinguishes

this daughter of love; her shape is remarkably genteel, and her figure good; she sings a good song, and is a chearful *bon* companion; her complexion is fair, her eyes, though grey, exceedingly melting, and seem to speak the disposition of the parts below very forcibly, and if you would wish to find a good bed-fellow, tho' not blest with every other perfection, this lady will perhaps suit her price, which is two pounds two.

Mrs T—rb—t, No 25, Titchfield-street.

> *The glow of youth, the fire of wanton love,*
> *Sports in her eye, and rouse the sensual heart*
> *To strong desires unmanageable pitch.*

So universally known, and so great a fav'rite with the bucks is this lady, that her description is almost needless; her eyes and hair are of the most inviting darkness, her temper and disposition good, and her mind replete with the choicest gifts of *Minerva*; her figure is elegant, she is very tall, sings and dances to perfection, and has only been in a *public* way of life twelve months; for a single skirmish she does not refuse the King's smallest picture, but for a whole night's siege expects three of the largest.

Miss R—ch—rds—n, No 2, Bennett-street, Rathbone-Place.

> *If women were as little as they are good,*
> *A peas cod would make them a gown and a hood.*

A pretty, little, lively, fair complexioned girl, with a dainty leg and foot, and as pretty a pair of pouting bubbies as ever went against a man's stomach, and one who well deserves the attention that is paid her by every man capable of knowing her value. She is pleasing, though fond, and can make wantonness delightful; every part assists to bring on the momentary delirium, and then each part combines to raise up the fallen member, to contribute again to repeated rapture; her price is commonly two guineas, but if the man is clever, she is very ready to make some abatement.

THE
Amorous Gallant's Tongue
Tipp'd with
GOLDEN EXPRESSIONS:
OR, THE
Art of Courtſhip refined.

Being the Beſt and Neweſt
ACADEMY.
CONTAINING

I. Choice and Select Sentences, or Forms of Courtſhip, to be uſed by Gentlemen and Ladies upon all Occaſions.

II. Variety of Choice Letters, written to both Sexes. relating to Love and Buſineſs.

III. The Interpretation of all Sorts of Dreams. With many other Things, both pleaſant and profitable to both Sexes.

To which is added,

Bills, Bonds, Releaſes, Letters of Attorney, Receipts and Acquittances upon all Occaſions.

TOGETHER WITH

A Canting Academy, or the *Pedlar's-French* Dictionary.

The Whole being very Uſeful and Neceſſary for all Perſons in general.

The Twelfth Edition.

LONDON: Printed for *J. Clarke*, in *Duc Lane*, *C. Hitch*, in *Pater-noſter row*, *J. Hodg* on *London-Bridge*, *T. King*, in *Moorefields*, and *T. Harris*, on *London-Bridge*. 1741

LOVE LETTERS

A rich old Gentleman to a fair young Virgin Lady.

Young Lady,

When you are once acquainted with me, I am sure the Greyness of my Hair will be no Obstacle to the Greenness of my Affection: for you will find me a young Lover, however you may now think me an old Man: and the Deficiency of my Person (if such Thing could be) will be abundantly made good with golden Charms. My Bags of Treasure shall be laid as Offering at your Feet, and you shall be their sole Disposer. Know this withal, young Lady, my Love shall be more staid, and more sincere, than those of younger Years; whose common Fault is to be guilty of Inconstancy, and to be always eager after Variety. Whereas, my self, happy in the Enjoyment of your Youth and Beauty, will never go astray. In Expectation of which Happiness, I make bold to subscribe my self, fairest Lady,

Your most affectionate Servant.

The Young Virgin's Answer:

Grave Sir,

I have received yours, and in Return must tell you, that I am already as well acquainted with you as I intend to be. And as to the Greenness of your Affection, give me Leave to say, you look more like an old Dotard, than a young Lover. Indeed, the best Argument you have is Gold, which I could very well dispense withal, were there not such a Clog tied to each Bag. Tho' Gold be one of the most precious Metals, yet when with sacred Love it stands in competition, it does appear to me but vilest Dross, and loses all its Excellency; and you must certainly either never have been acquainted with Love, or else have quite forgotten it, to think one of my Years and Beauty could prefer Gold before it. You think, I believe, a mighty Argument to draw me to you, when you tell me, that young Men are oft inconstant, and love Variety. But were such young Men married, as you'd have me to be, I could not blame 'em for it, nor think it any Crime: nay, I believe that in those Circumstances I should do the like. It makes me blush to read what you have written about enjoying of my Youth and Beauty. Sure you cannot think me so insensible, as to exchange the Flower of my Youth for such a Bundle of Mortality? You may as soon join May to cold December, as hope that you and I should e'er be married. Sixteen and Seventy are too great a Distance ever to meet together. Go then, and wed your Gold, make that your Mistress, and so put Earth to Earth. Gold may do well when join'd with Youth and Beauty; but Gold without a Man, is but bad Logick in the School of Love. And now you know my Mind, take my Advice; be thinking of your Grave, and not of Love, and wed yourself to Heaven against you die, and then I shall be thankful, if you'll bequeath those Bags of Gold you boast of, to

Your young Adviser.

A Lady to her despairing Lover, who had given over his Suit at the first Repulse.

Sir,

You are certainly but a fresh Soldier in the Wars of *Cupid*, or else you would never have quitted the Siege for the first Repulse. It seems below the Resolution of a Lover to give over his Pretensions at the first Denial, and makes him forget the Proverb, *That faint Heart never won fair Lady*. I believe there are few Lovers but what expect to meet with Repulses, it being consistent with the Modesty of our Sex, to say Nay at the first asking: nay, I am confident, should I have done so, yourself would have condemned me of Levity. And I appeal to all the Scholars in the School of Love, whether too much Forwardness do not turn a Lover's Stomach. But she that at first denies only out of a Conformity to Custom, may at the same Time have that Respect for a Lover, which it would be very proper not for to discover, till she has first had some Experience of his Truth and Constancy; which would be then too late to try, when once the Fort is yielded up. You may see, Sir, by these Steps that I have made to meet you, what a Prospect you have of Success in our next Assault, and how little Reason you have to be discouraged by your first Repulse. For, notwithstanding what I said at that Time, you may easily guess by what I have written, that I have no Aversion for you. And in Witness thereof, subscribe my self, Sir,

Your Servant in all honourable Things.

The fearful Lover to his supposed inconstant Mistress.

Madam,

It is now evident, That nothing is more vain, than to believe a Woman can speak Truth: for what is it you have left unsaid to persuade me of your Truth and Constancy; and yet how apparently have you broken all your Vows, as if they had never been made? And that too without the least Occasion given? For I am sure I never had a Thought that went astray from that sincere Affection I have for you; and which is still the same as ever: and can you be unkind, unjust, and false to such a Lover? Have a care, Madam, of changing your Adorer for another, lest he should prove as false to you, as you have been to me, and so your Sin be made your Punishment. But, Madam, since I am still the same I was, why should not you be so and so compleat that Happiness, which I shall never hope for in another? Since I am so fixedly resolved ever to remain,

Your most devoted Servant.

Her Answer.

My dear Incredulous?

I received your upbraiding Letter; and were it not that I see it springs from Jealousy, which is the Child of Love, I should return another Sort of Answer than what I am about to write, and let you know, that you deserve to have your Words made good against you, *that there is nothing more vain than to believe a Woman can speak Truth*: but your Love attones for your Rashness. Since you write I have so apparently broken all my Vows, pray let me know wherein it does appear. For what's apparent must be very evident. Have I disown'd to you my Passion for you, or permitted the Addresses of another? If neither of these two, wherein is it apparent? Why I dis-owned my Love, it seems, to one that questioned me about it: 'tis very like I might; for what have I to do to satisfy the impertinent Curiosity of every one that asks me a Question? Who made him an Examiner, had been Answer enough; but I was minded he should know nothing of it; for that I saw was his Design, and I was resolved he should miss his Aim. I have absolutely refused both the Addresses and the Company of several that have pretended to be my Servants, as they themselves will be ready to attest, which makes it more apparent, that I remember still, and keep my Vows to you: and therefore let me beg you, Sir, to make your self and me more easie for the Time to come; because I know not how such unkind Usage, when without all Reason, may alienate that Love which hitherto I have not varied from, no, not in Thought. Let it content you then, that I am still, and still resolve to be,

Your constant Lover.

A Letter from a young Woman, to one who had gotten her with Child.

Dear Sir,

I need not, nay I cannot, give you a greater Demonstration of my Love to you, than what I have already given; for I have given up (to satisfie your importunate Desires) that only Jewel that was worth the keeping; and which to keep inviolable, is the only Boast of our Sex. You know how solemnly you promised me Marriage, before I admitted you to those Favours; and since I have hazarded my Reputation to give you Satisfaction, I hope you will take Care to prevent that Reproach that is likely to fall upon me, by my being with Child. And as it is the Fruit of your own Importunities, more than of my Desires, so I hope you will no longer defer the performing your Promise, and so save the Reputation both of my self and the Child I am big with, who will other-wise be esteemed a Bastard, which its being born in Wedlock will prevent. And tho' I know that many have suffered Shipwreck, and split upon that Rock on which I have ventured, yet I hope you will prove your self a Man of that Veracity, as to bring me with Honour to the safe Harbour of your wish'd for Marriage-Bed; where we may, without a Blush, enjoy those Pleasures, which by being Criminal, lose much of their Sweetness: but then it will be an Addition to my Happiness, that I shall be always

Yours, etc.

The young Man's Answer.

My *Quondam* Mistress,

I indeed promised you Marriage when you were a Virgin, but I never promised to marry a Whore, under which odious Character you now appear. If it be a good Excuse to say you yielded to my Importunities, how know I but another may be as importunate as my self, and you as yielding to him, as you have been to me: and who wou'd wed himself, on the continual Fear of being made a Cuckold? It concerns me, I believe, to take Care of the Infant, and of its Reputation too; which may be effected without our Marriage, it being a Thing I am resolved against; for I have lately heard, That he who lies with a Woman first, and marries her afterwards, is like one that puts a Sir-reverence in his Hat, and afterwards puts it on his Head, which I believe few Men delight to do. If in any Thing else I can make you Recompence, I will; but as to Marriage, I must beg your Pardon, resolving never in that Kind to be

Yours, etc.

A NEW

ATALANTIS,

FOR

The Year One thousand seven
hundred and Fifty-eight.

Omnia Vincit amor, nos et cedamus amori.
VIRG.

Love conquers all, let us that God obey.

The SECOND EDITION.

LONDON:
Printed for M. THRUSH in Salisbury-Court,
Fleet-Street. 1758.

ESSESIA

The delicate Essesia was composed of most sensitive fibres. Through her father, she derived her privilege of living free. He was one of mirth's jovial crew, of true bacchanalian inclinations; had a pretty turn for ballad-making, and was an occasional messenger of the supreme.

Essesia, not to prove degenerate from her fire, felt early the inklings of nature, and set about indulging them. When turned of twelve, and at the boarding-school, grown quite tired of all niggard and unsocial pleasure, she resolved to have a partner in her raptures; which was difficult to effect on account of her confinement, and the inspection she was under: this greatly mortifying her, drew on a slight fever, on account of which, in order to forward her recovery, she was moved to a lodging on Blackheath for the benefit of the air.

In the same house young Clerimont lodged, who had been lately brought thither from the academy, in order to recover from a menaced consumption; which some attributed to too close a study of his books; others to too great an application to himself. Whatever might have been the cause, it diffused a delicate languor over his complexion, which Essesia, from the natural partiality and good opinion the sex has of itself, soon construed into a passion for her.

In this opinion she was confirmed by the respectful looks, and tip-toe attention Clerimont paid her on all occasions. He took care to be before-hand with all her desires, in presenting her every thing she wanted. When-ever she walked abroad, he was her constant attendant.

The people of the house, and those charged with the care of them, were so pleased with the mutual and tender politeness they showed to each other, that they called it the triumph of innocent friendship. Nay, so little did their guardians dream of any harm, that they were often let to walk abroad over the Heath to Greenwich park, or any other place they chose; so absolute a reliance was on their virtue. Nature whispered soft desires to them both; while Cupid on one side, and Venus on the other, marked them out for mutual instructions to each other.

Clerimont now and then would surprise a kiss from her, for

which she would call him, 'vastly rude and naughty'; then the sly lurcher affecting to drop a tear, she, good natured soul, would give him another kiss to reconcile matters, and dissipate his pretended affliction.

Clerimont grown more forward, and she less coy; he at last not only offered to put his hand into her bosom, but even to draw up the curtain of her lower altar. At which violence she stormed. He then artfully bled at the nose, which, to the sex, unquestionable proof of love, disarmed her. He some time after threw himself on his knees, and having kissed her hand, dewed it with tears, and put it into his bosom next his skin, that she might feel how his fond heart beat repentance, and hoped she would forgive him; which she did, and joined her tears to his. This kiss of peace being given, and tears dried up, they walked home arm in arm as if nothing had happened.

Clerimont having procured a key of Greenwich park, he lured out Essesia at the dusk of the evening, to One-tree-hill. Where, as they sat under the reverend shade, which has been the confident of many a tender tale, and declaration of love, he threw one hand amorously about her neck, and said, 'my dear Essesia, we are made for each other': then to kindle a passion in her, with closely applied and repeated kisses, he made her lips quiver. Almost vanquished, and yielding to his desires, she was farther electrified by an azure tinctured snow bolt, tipt with fire, which he had conveyed into her hand. But alarmed by the last remains of modesty, she broke loose, and ran from him with precipitation down a slope; he after her into a close thicket, where unfortunately she was tript up by some branches which got hold of her cloaths. Some say it was Cupid did it. She, however, fell gently on a bed of fern, which that god had prepared.

While victorious Clerimont, after some little resistance, rather exciting than disgusting, enjoyed consummate happiness; Cupid with a number of attendant genii soared exultingly over them. They waved their silver wings, which dashing their rays one against the other, induced the sagacious observators at Flamstead-house, to level their long tubes at, proclaim it the *Aurora borealis*, and prick it down in their note-book.

After the solemn rites were over, she railed at first, then burst into a flood of tears, and asked him, 'how he dared to use her so': his soothing reply was, 'that she being so charming, how could he have done other-wise'. Her next exclamation was, 'I am ruined.' 'How ruined,' quoth he, 'to be adored by the tenderest heart that ever felt the power of love? Had I been longer without possessing, I must have perished; and should you now declare, I never shall see you again; rather than survive such a sentence, here take this poinard, and thrust it into a wretched heart, which can never, not only know happiness, but even desire existence, if separated from you.'

These words, uttered in a most affectionate manner, and accompanied with tears, quite won her to him; and she proposed, 'as a proof of your sincerity, let us vow a constant love to each other'. No sooner mentioned, than they both dropped devoutly on their knees. While in their declarations, they poured forth all the impassionate dictates of romance; Cupid, who frolicked over them in the air, blew their vows from him, to his basking genii, who sportfully puffed them from one to another.

Home returned the reconciled parties, and eleven next night was the appointed hour of rendezvous; at which time Clerimont was to steal privately to her chamber, and those who attended her to bed, quitted her at ten.

At breakfast next morning, they looked chearfully on each other, and their eyes sparkling with such unusual lustre, made all about them prognosticate for their health, since so great and sudden a change had happened in them for the better.

How many tender squeezes in the day! How often did they whisper to each other kind complaints against the slow approach of night! How long did it appear to them from breakfast to dinner! Longer still from dinner to supper! But from supper to bed time was almost eternity!

However, long-wished for eleven arriving at last, he stole softly to her chamber door; on which he gave Monimia's signal. Three soft knocks gained admittance; he flew with her instantly into bed. For two hours it was all riot and excess of love. After which, in order to recruit their exhausted strength, they indulged the kind approach of sleep.

He awoke first, and by a lamp hung from the tester of the bed, the curtains closely drawn, that they might mutually enjoy the pleasure of seeing and examining each other, he gazed upon her charms, and hung over her enamoured. Her face was as smooth as polished marble. She smiled in every feature. Her ruby lips seemed to move, and invite him to a kiss, which he fondly impresses. Then with desiring eyes, greedily surveys his sleeping goddess. He kisses every part, uncertain where to fix, tossed to and fro, in a variety of beauteous excellence.

To the raptures of seeing, he makes those of feeling succeed, his hand now sliding gently down her well-turned neck, now moulding the budding orbs on her breast, now with full sweep strays along, until it cover the alcove of bliss with fervent zeal; at which inspiriting touch, the watchful centinel there gives the alarm to his mistress, who instantly awakes and joins issue.

Having finished their morning sacrifice, the youth returned by times to his chamber, before any of the family was stirring, to avoid giving the least room for suspicion.

From a frequency of those interviews, Essesia grew better, but Clerimont became quite emaciated. His physicians ordered him to the south of France, which he was glad of, being quite tired of the constant drudgery Essesia exacted from him.

He therefore, under pretence of a visit to some friends in London, without any farewell declaration to her, put an end to the amour, and set out with a governor for France. The rage which such an ungrateful treatment threw Essesia into, was productive of one advantage to her, by causing a miscarriage. Having alternately wept, and raged; condemned her own folly; and exclaimed against the perfidy of men, she in a short time forgot her faithless lover.

Her parents having received information of her being better in health, sent for her to their house in London; fully resolved to marry her as soon as possible, knowing well that maiden-ladies at best are but brittle ware, and that she would prove much more so, if she took after either of themselves.

She was carried to all public places, and a great deal of company invited to the house, in hopes of an opportunity of getting her off. Essesia's favourite amusement was to ride in the park, where she contrived for herself a loco-motive enjoyment.

She had been so startled at the thoughts of pregnancy by her false Clerimont, that she was resolved never to endanger her reputation with any of the deceitful villains, till such time as she should be under matrimonial cover. She could dexterously fix to her saddle, when on it, a most artificial representative of Priapus; and in a proper position to metaphysically enjoy which ever of her attendant admirers on horse-back, she liked the best for that time. In proportion to her worked up degree of passion, she hastened or retarded her horse's gait.

But a husband being soon procured for her, she abandoned shadowy raptures, in order to enjoy real ones. Having made the Economy of love her favourite book, she from thence had learned the medicaments to close up chasms caused (through an indulgence of passion), by way of a maidenhead restorative. And this she executed according to art; nay, played the part of the suffering virgin's part so well the first night, that the booby husband thought himself a very vigorous man. He took all manner of pains to comfort Essesia, by assuring her use would make things go easier. She was obliged to bite her tongue, in order to refrain from laughing at the taken in, and credulous nincompoop.

The sluggish duties of Hymen no way answering the rapidity of her desires, she fell into a melancholy, which to sooth, as she was one day sauntering up the queen's walk towards the bason on the hill, she was accosted by the good lady Rocforia, ever bountiful in advice to redress female grievances.

'How comes it, dear Essesia, that you look so gravely, who have been lately married?' 'That is just the cause,' replied Essesia with a sigh. 'How, in the name of mutual bliss, is not your husband a —?' 'He is one among the crowd of husbands,' rejoined Essesia very demurely, 'but such scanty pittance can never satisfy so keen an appetite as mine. I am therefore resolved to try experiments.'

'In point of experiments, my dear Essesia, I can communicate some observations of mine, which may hereafter be of service to you. Like yourself, I soon found marriage-dues were far short of my expectations. Whether from the imbecility of the fellow, or that he carried his offerings to other altars. I cannot say. I therefore resolved to apply for succour to all who should appear pleasing to me at home and abroad. All have their virtues. Their faults appeared to me as follow.

'Our countrymen, from a constitutional gloomy habit, are always for making deep and useless researches. They dwell too long upon a thing, without any intermediate Relievos, which is very disagreeable to their assistants.

'The volatility of the French, who always play on, or about the surface, by their continual skipping up and down, is highly

201

irritating, but not at all satisfying. I have been frequently obliged to use a slap to them.

'The Italians are so profoundly respectful, and so protestingly tedious, that more of the ceremonial is to be met with amongst them than any thing else. So fond are they of over-shooting the mark, and keep so awful a distance from what we love to have ever closely approached to, that by most nations they are looked upon as very backward in love.

'The Germans or High-Dutch are in the service of Venus; as in that of Mars. To act heroic deeds in either, they must be roused with spirituous liquors. The phlegmatic Low-Dutch are very apt to fall asleep in the trenches. Wherefore, to rouze and keep them awake, the martinet and finger-spurs are absolutely necessary.'

Essesia, who had hitherto listened to Rocforia with great attention, at the last image burst into a fit of laughter – to which Rocforia said, 'you may laugh, child, but all I have advanced is true. However, not to lose any more time in idle digression, I will put you in a way of obtaining the frequentation and plenitude you are in need of. You must know, dear Essesia, that having had always at heart the relieving family-deficiencies of our sex, for, as the humane Dido says,

'Non ignara mali miseris succurrere te disco.'

'A sufferer myself, I bring comfort to the sufferings of others: my house is a stated rendezvous for people of fashion of both sexes. There is not a gayer circle in town: for thither come the young princes of the illustrious house of Bunwick. This is to be one of my nights; so thither come, Essesia. Fortune attend you, and make good what Hymen has proved a bankrupt to you in.'

Essesia dropped her a most profound courtesy of gratitude, protesting she would not fail: the two ladies parted mutually pleased, one in hopes of receiving succour; the other in high glee, that she should be the means of procuring it.

Evening come, Essesia, who had ransacked art to equip herself in all the elegance of dress, went to Rocforia's, whither she was preceded by half a dozen select livery-men carrying flambeaus so widely flaring, that the streets thro' which she passed, seemed all in a blaze. Thus our modern Thais was lighted along in quest of some vigorous Alexander to lay her flames.

If Essesia was agreeably surprised at seeing so brilliant a company, they for some time gazed with a pleased astonishment, alternately admiring the consummate taste of her attire, and the lively expression of her features.

Prince Edeling, on the first sight, was so smitten that he could not conceal his emotions. Which the quick-sighted and commodious Rocforia (who had a look-out every where) perceiving, communicated her discovery aside to Essesia: and observed to her what a distinguished pleasure it must be, to have the first squeezing of a twig of the royal oak. Essesia reddened, and made no other than the old hackened reply, 'O, you flatter me'; but a dance of joy was in her heart at the same time.

Rocforia went to the prince, entered into a conversation with him about indifferent matters, and so imperceptibly to him, tho' pleasingly, directed his movements, that he came up where Essesia was. Then Rocforia, according to her assumed office, introduced them to each other.

In the prince's compliments to her were all the stammering and confusion of a young-lover. She answered on her side with affected timidity and studied diffidence. Essesia, a true woman, feeling the prince to be her undoubted conquest, not to pall upon his eyes, and to excite a regret of her, made an early retreat. Which female artifice, Rocforia understanding very well, did not labour to oppose.

Having descried the prince's sudden dejection after the departure of Essesia, to whom in consequence the room seemed void of company; nay, every place was uneasy; she went up to him, and most submissively enquired if his royal highness was displeased at any thing that had happened in her house, which would prove a very great mortification to her.

'Displeased in part I am,' replied the prince to Rocforia; 'but, on the whole, have never been so pleased. Let us retire to another room, there I will pour out my heart to you, and make you confident of what it feels', which was immediately done.

'Displeased I am (continued the prince) at Essesia's early departure; but in my life have never been so pleased with any woman. If there were any hopes, Rocforia! – Yes, it is in her power to make the happiest of mortals – but she is married, and I despair.'

'Married, a fiddle-stick (quoth Rocforia, with some warmth

on her own account) 'marriage is no argument among people of fashion and quality, but rather a convenient covering for gallantry. – I am ashamed of your mentioning despair. Let me inform you, prince, for I have a pretty general knowledge of the world, that in love as in war, no place has been ever got, but after an attack.'

'I understand you well (said Edeling), but how form it without causing scandal? There is no going to the husband's house.' 'No, to be sure (joined Rocforia), but you may write a letter to Essesia, which, thro' me, shall be conveyed safely to her hands, without any danger of its falling into the husband's.'

At this Edeling ran to her, gave a long-winded kiss of thanks, and said, 'In the morning I will send you a letter to be forwarded to Essesia.' – To which she curtsied, 'Rely on Rocforia, who shall always think herself in duty bound to contribute to your private amusements.'

The prince and Essesia in the night dreamt of each other. As imagination played her part in visionary raptures, the prince cried out, 'O lovely Essesia, the immortals are not more happy than I am in thy arms': and thus she, in her fancied joys, 'O my sweet prince Edeling, Hymen can give no transports like these you excite.'

As soon as up in the morning, his imagination still warmed with the transactions of the night, the prince wrote the following letter:

To the divine ESSESIA.

Charming beyond expression, since the first moment your radiant eyes shot passion into me, I have felt, I know not how, and with the utmost impatience sigh for another interview. While separated from you, to me time crawls irksomely along. The emotions of my heart are so tempestuous, in the name of love, do you appoint a rendezvous to calm them, and relieve from farther agony,

your devoted
EDELING.

The convenient go-between Rocforia, having delivered the letter, was consulted what should be done. Her advice to Essesia was to go that evening to the Marrubian-gardens, a place of public diversion, and of which the prince should be informed.

Essesia failed not to go thither, nor the prince to meet her there. Having made a turn or two in the walks, they went into a kind of alcove, shut the door, and remained there about half an hour. When they came out, they appeared somewhat flurried. But what they had said or done to each other, no one can tell.

About this time Rocforia was come to offer her service in any article that might be wanted. Her coming was very apropos, for both the prince and Essesia confessed to her their having mutually agreed to make each other happy; but they sunk the expedition in the alcove.

As soon as they mentioned their distress to her, about a safe and convenient place to pass the night in, Rocforia bid them banish all uneasiness on that head; for that her husband was gone to a horse-race fifty miles distant, and therefore she could accommodate them for that night.

The enamoured pair went with her. She gave them an elegant supper, and put them to bed unknown to any servant in the house. How long this kind intercourse continued by the intermediation of Rocforia, is a secret which future annalists of love may reveal.

HOW A GENTLEMAN THAT FELL IN LOVE
WITH ANOTHER MAN'S WIFE,
THROUGH THE ADVICE OF A BAWD,
ENJOY'D HER, AND UPON WHAT TERMS,
AND WHAT HAPPEN'D THEREUPON.

An Amorous Spark having observ'd a very fine Woman sitting in a *Goldsmith's* Shop behind the Counter, was so much taken with her, that nothing wou'd serve him, but enjoying her; which yet he was altogether at a loss how to accomplish, having no manner of Acquaintance either with her or her Husband. In this hopeless condition he goes to a Bawd, who had several times assisted him in his Love-Intrigues, and tells her at what a *non-plus* he was to accomplish his Design. The Bawd at first persuades him off of her, and promises to help him to one that shall not only equal, but surpass her. But all that was in vain, for nothing wou'd satisfie but only this very Person. Well, says this Mistress in the Mystery of Iniquity, I'll tell you how you shall obtain your purpose, if you are resolv'd to pursue it. Do but that, says he, and you'll oblige me for ever. – Well then, says she, you must take an opportunity to go into the Shop when she's there, and buy some little Trifle or other of her, or her Husband, and repeat this often, buying sometimes one thing, and sometimes another, till by degrees you have brought your self acquainted with her and her Husband, and in so doing you can't miss of an opportunity to sound her Inclinations: if Pleasure has the Ascendant over her, you'll gain your Point the sooner; but if Money be the Idol she adores, you must attack her with Gifts, and making Presents to her, and you cannot fail of prevailing. The Gentleman lik'd her Counsel very well, and was resolv'd to take it: and accordingly took an opportunity to buy a Silver *Snuff-Box*; and having before bought some fine Walnuts, he presented his Mistress with some, and by cracking of them, had an opportunity to tarry longer in the Shop, and gaze more on that Beauty which had already overcome him. In two or three Days after, he comes again, and buys half a dozen Silver Spoons and Forks, and then brought some Peaches to his Mistress, and presents her with them; and a Week after buys some other odd things, and still brought something or other which he presented to his Mistress; who always look'd upon it as the Effect of his good Nature, and affable Temper, and had no apprehension of his being her humble Servant. After he had drove this Trade of being a constant Customer to the Shop for several Weeks together, and had made no farther progress of his Amours, save to be look'd on as a Friend and Acquaintance, and once or twice invited to Dinner; at one of which times her Husband was call'd down into the Shop to a Customer, in which interim he took an opportunity to acquaint her somewhat darkly with his Passion, which she either did not, or wou'd not understand; so that he begun almost to despair, and complain'd to the Bawd how much Charge he had been at, and what little likelihood there was of attaining his End. The Bawd told him, he had no reason yet to complain; for having got an Acquaintance there, and once discover'd his Passion, he had brought things to a pretty good forwardness; my advice therefore now is, said she, that you let her fully know your Mind, and solicite her for the last Favour; and let me know your success, and then I'll tell you how you shall proceed.

He once more takes her Counsel, and going to cheapen some *Knick-knacks* there, he finds her all alone; and having bought something of her, letting it lie upon the Counter, Madam, says he, I have made many Errands hither, but 'tis for your sake; for you are my chief Business, and your Incomparable and Peerless Beauty has made that Impression in my Heart, as will put a sudden Period to my Life, unless your Compassion will grant me a Reprieve; for nothing can retrieve it, but the Enjoyment of your Love and Beauty. – I can't believe, Sir, says she, that that poor Stock of Beauty I am Owner of, can ever produce any such fatal Effects as those you speak of: but 'tis the common Theme you are pleas'd to entertain our Sex withal, tho' there be nothing in it. However, 'tis methinks a great piece of Folly to love at that rate, where you can have no hopes of Enjoyment; for I am otherwise dispos'd of: and there are young Ladies enough that are single, that are more worthy of you. I question not, Madam, *reply'd he*, but I might have choice of Mistresses: but 'tis you only that have wounded me, and therefore 'tis you alone that can effect my Cure. – What wou'd you have me do to cure you, Sir, said she? Do, Madam, said he! Grant me the Enjoyment of your Love, for that alone can give me ease. Why said she, wou'd you have me wrong my Husband's Bed? Shou'd I do so, how do you think he'd take it? E'en bad enough, I believe, if he shou'd know it; but sure there's no necessity of that: and if you keep your Counsel, I shall take nothing from him he can miss. – Hold, Sir, says she, you talk as if we were already agreed, but you shall find there will be two words to that Bargain. Besides, you don't – but here's my Husband coming, says the Jilt – indeed, Sir, I have sold you a Pennyworth, I'll be judg'd by my Husband. (Her Husband coming then into the Shop.) The Gentleman perceiving how cunningly she turn'd off her Discourse, told her, he did believe she hadn't wrong'd him much, and he was satisfy'd. And then shewing her Husband what he had bought, and what he paid for it, he told him his Wife had us'd him very well: and so took his leave of 'em, and went to his old Crone the Bawd, and told her what had pass'd. You may depend upon it, says the Bawd, that she'll comply; but you must Fee her pretty high, or it won't do. This made him shrug; for tho' he had a great mind to enjoy her, he was not willing to be at too much Charge: which the old Bawd perceiving, told him he cou'd not expect to carry her under a Present of at least Fifty Guineas: but yet, says she, if you will give me but Five, I'll warrant you, shall gain your Point without being at any charge at all. Make but that out, says he, and I'll promise you the five Guineas as soon as e'er I've enjoy'd her. No, Sir, says the Bawd, I'll have my Mony in hand, for you know we never trust. Well, says he, here's your Mony, and giving it into her Hand, now let me know your method. Upon which the Bawd thus began.

Before I proceed, pray tell me the Price of that Diamond Ring you wear upon your Finger. Why what wou'd you do with that, replies the Beau; I wou'dn't part with my Ring for an hundred Guineas, for it cost me above Fourscore, and I had a great Pennyworth in it; and if you'd have me to give her that, this is all Trick and Cheat; and I am only funn'd out of five Guineas for nothing. Why so hasty, says the Bawd? I design no such matter; but you won't hear me out: Go to the Goldsmith, and tell him you are disappointed of a Bill that you expected out of the Country, and that you have a present occasion for fifty

Guineas, which you must desire him to let you have, and you'll leave that Ring as a Pledge in the mean time; and that as soon as your Bill comes to Town, which you expect every day, you'll pay him again. This Kindness he won't deny you, because he runs no hazard in it, and thereby he obliges a Customer. When you have got these fifty Guineas, take the first opportunity to discourse your Mistress; if you find she'll do it for Love, your Mony is sav'd, and you have nothing else to do but enjoy her; but if the Jade be Mercenary, you must tempt her with Gold, and that you may be sure to make her bite; give her the fifty Guineas that you borrow'd of her Husband. – A Pox take ye for an old Bitch, says he, in a kind of Passion; is this the way to bring me off for nothing? – You are too hasty still, replies the Bawd; let me have done first, and then talk your Pleasure: do as I say, give her the fifty Guineas; and when you have enjoy'd her, stay with her, either in the Chamber or the Shop, till her Husband does come in; and when you see him, tell him you have receiv'd the Bill that you expected, and have brought the fifty Guineas that you borrow'd of him, and paid it to his Wife; and so desire him to let you have your Ring again. His Wife (to save her Honour) can do no less than own she has receiv'd the Mony; and so her Husband must restore your Ring. And then do you be judge whether or no you don't come off for nothing. Well, thou'rt a dear sweet Rogue for this Contrivance, says he, and I could almost kiss thee, but that thy Mouth's so strongly guarded by thy Nose and Chin, there's no coming at it: I like thy Plot extreamly well, and I'll go presently and put it in Execution.

Away goes the Fop, as well pleas'd to think he shou'd put a Trick on his Mistress, as he shou'd enjoy her, which for the lucre of the fifty Guineas he no longer question'd. And coming to the Goldsmith's Shop, he pulls his Ring off of his Finger, and asks him what he'll give for't; the Goldsmith having look'd upon it, told him he'd give Seventy Guineas for't. It cost me more than Eighty, says the Beau, but I won't part with it; only because I'm short of Mony, being disappointed of a Bill that I expected to receive, I must desire the kindness of you to let me have fifty Guineas on it till I receive my Bill, which will be in a Fortnight or three Weeks time at farthest; and I'll allow you what you shall think reasonable for it. The Goldsmith very readily gives him the fifty Guineas he desir'd, and takes his Ring as a Security. And so taking his leave, goes home very well satisfy'd he had proceeded thus far prosperously.

In two or three Days after, he goes to make a Visit to the Goldsmith's Wife; and it fell out in such a lucky Minute, that her Husband was from home, whereby he had an opportunity with the more freedom to renew his Suit; and tho' he arm'd himself with all the Charms he cou'd, taking the Auxiliary Helps both of the *Tayler*, *Barber* and *Perfumer*; yet it all wou'd not do: fain he'd have sav'd running the hazard of his fifty Guineas; but when he found he cou'd not without such a Present obtain his wish'd Enjoyment, he at last address'd her thus: well, Madam, I do perceive you are of kin to *Danae*, whom *Jove* himself could not prevail upon, till he courted her in Showers of Gold, and that dissolv'd her quickly into Love; and I intend to follow his Example, and to enjoy your Favour I make this Present to you, and therewithal gave her the fifty Guineas. And this had so soon mollify'd her Stubbornness, and made her maleable, that she straight made him this agreeable Return: Well, Sir, I see you're so much a Gentleman, that I scarce know how to deny you any longer: your amiable Person and good Humour has overcome me so, I can no longer make Resistance, but offer myself to your Embraces. The Gallant then enquir'd if all were safe below, and if they shou'd not be in danger of meeting any Interruption from her Husband. She bid him never fear, all was secure enough: and then conducting him into the Chamber, she let him have what he so much desir'd. When he had thus debauch'd her, and satisfy'd his Lustful Appetite, he ask'd her how long 'twould be e're her Husband wou'd be at home? She told him, he was gone out of Town, and wou'd not be at home these Ten-days. At which he seem'd to be surpriz'd, for he was loth to be without his Ring so long; but since there was no Remedy, he was resolv'd to wait till he came home. His Mistress seeing him so indifferent at the hearing of her Husband's absence, cou'dn't tell what to think shou'd be the reason of it; and ask'd him what 'twas troubled him? Nothing, my Dear, said he, but I was thinking how crosly things fell out; because my own Affairs obliges me to be some Days out of Town just at this happy Juncture, when I might have been blest so oft with your Embraces. The cunning Baggage (now she had

got his fifty Guineas) was as indifferent as he for that, and told him, time might present 'em with another opportunity which might be full as favourable: And so they parted.

The Spark was satisfy'd with the Enjoyment of his Lady, and that Itch now was cur'd; he only wanted back his Ring, or his fifty Guineas, that he might demand it of her Husband; and now reflecting on his short-liv'd Pleasure, he truly judg'd that he had bought it at too dear a Rate, altho' he should be only at the five Guineas Charge he gave the Bawd.

But since the Goldsmith's being out of Town was such a *Disappointment*, as cou'd not be foreseen, and yet had been extremely serviceable to him in the Enjoyment of his Mistress, he goes to the old Bawd, and gives her an account of what had pass'd, and asks her further how he must proceed in getting of his Ring again, without repaying of the fifty Guineas? Give me the other Fee, says the old Jade, and I'll inform you; for I am like a Lawyer, and don't know how to speak without a Fee. No, no, says he, I have Feed enough before, nor wou'd I give so much again for all the Pleasure her Enjoyment gave me. – The Bawd (since she saw nothing more was to be got by him) advises him to wait the Goldsmith's coming home, and then take a fit opportunity to go to her alone, and to pretend he was just come to Town; and to desire another Assignation from her; which being made, and you having once more enjoy'd her, stay till her Husband comes, and do as you were first directed. And when you have got your Ring again, I hope you'll then present me with two Guineas more, – no, not a Farthing more, says he; you know I paid you very well before-hand: And so left her.

The Bawd perceiving nothing more was to be got from him, resolv'd she wou'd be even with him, and take *another course* to make a Penny of him: and thereupon goes the next Morning to the Goldsmith's Shop, and asks the Prentice if his Mistress was within? He answers, Yes; and she reply'd, she must needs speak with her: who coming down, the Bawd whispers her in the Ear, that she had something to acquaint her with, of great Importance to her, which was not at to be discours'd of publickly: and thereupon the Mistress ask'd her to walk up, and leading of her into a With-drawing-Room, desir'd her to sit down; and then intreated her to tell her Business: upon which the Bawd began as followeth.

Madam, *Altho' I am a Stranger to you, I doubt not but you will excuse the rudeness of this Visit, when you shall know 'twas only the Concern I have to see a Lady of your Worth and Beauty so much design'd upon and trick'd, as you are like to be, that has occasion'd it: I know therefore, Madam, that there's a Gentleman, who has been for some time a great Admirer of your matchless Beauty, which truly does deserve all those Encomiums that I have often heard him justly give it: this Gentleman, under the Notion of a Customer, has made you many Visits: and has been pleas'd (I know not for what reason) to make me his Confident; of which I need give you no further Instance, than that he has acquainted me, that but a few Days past he gave you fifty Guineas, for which by way of Gratitude, he was admitted to enjoy your last Favours:* – Here the young Lady interrupted her, all blushing and confus'd: Madam, you've fully satisfy'd me, *said she*, that that false Man has let you know my Weakness, and most ungratefully expos'd my Honour, and betray'd me to the World. – *Nay, Madam*, said the Bawd, *be not so passionate; I don't believe he has acquainted any with it but my self. Nor let the Thoughts of that at all disturb you; for that's a Crime that I have known, for more than thirty Years, the rest of our Sex has scarce been free from. But that which more stirs up my Spleen against him, is for the Trick he designs to put upon you still; which is the only reason of my giving you this trouble.* You will oblige me in it very much, *reply'd the Goldsmith's Wife. Then this*, says the Bawd, *it is. He understands your Husband is now out of Town, and will be so for seven or eight Days time. As soon as he comes home, your Gallant will be with you to appoint him a time in which he may again enjoy your favour; which when he has enjoy'd, he does intend to tarry till your Husband shall come in, and then acquaint him that he has paid to you the fifty Guineas he borrow'd on his Ring; and so desire that he may have his Ring again; which is the thing he aims at. For he knows, that when you shall be ask'd whether or no you receiv'd the fifty Guineas, your Honour is so far concern'd, you can't deny it.* O Treacherous Villain! *said the She-Goldsmith with some Indignation*, is this the Generosity he so much boasted of? *Yes, Madam*, says the Bawd, *this is what he designs to do: but I am so concern'd to see a Lady of your Worth so basely impos'd upon, I could not but discover it: and if you wou'd be rul'd by me, you shou'd out-trick the Fop, and catch him in the Snare he'd lay for you.* – O I'd do any thing to be reveng'd on him, *cry'd the young Lady with some eagerness:* and do but tell me how, and keep my Counsel, and I'll so well reward you for your Pains that you shall say I am grateful – *Then, Madam,* says the *Bawd, as soon as your Husband comes to Town, before he comes to know of it, send one to tell him, that you must needs speak with him about earnest Business; and when he's come, tell him that you expect your Husband the next Day; and therefore beg the Favour of him to let you have his Company that Night; and as an earnest of your Love to him, and that he shou'd not think you mercenary, you'll both return him the fifty Guineas, and give him back the Ring your Husband have in Pawn. And tell him likewise, you have engag'd the Maid to Secrecy; for which if he presents her with a Guinea, 'tis all he need to do. This will, I am sure, engage him; for he is as Covetous as he is Lustful. And when he's thus engag'd, in the next place, acquaint your Husband how you cou'd scarce have any quiet in his absence from this young Spark's continual Solicitations to unlawful Love: then tell him that you have appointed him to come that Evening, of which you thought fit to acquaint him, that he might give him that Correction which he saw necessary, to cool his too hot Blood; this will so much confirm your Husband in his Opinion of your inviolable Chastity, that all your Treacherous Gallant shall offer to the contrary will be look'd upon as the effect of Malice and Revenge. Thus you'll confirm your Reputation to the World, and keep those fifty Guineas he designs to cheat you of, and be sufficiently reveng'd on an ungrateful Man.*

Well, says the injur'd Gentlewoman, *I am pleas'd with your Contrivance; but keep my Counsel, and you shall see my Vengeance on this ungrateful Wretch; and with how just a Retribution I shall use him for his intended Villany. And that you may be sensible you have not left your Labour, accept of this –* and therewithal put Ten Guineas in her hand, and promis'd her a farther Token of her Gratitude, and so dismist her.

The Bawd was well pleas'd with the Mornings Work she'd made; and finding that the Goldsmith's Wife was like to be the better Customer, she hugg'd her self for her Contrivance, and her Treachery to the Cully Beau.

That Afternoon the *wrathful Lady* receiv'd a Letter from her Husband, that he intended to be in Town the *Thursday* following, and desir'd her to meet him that Day at *Hammersmith* about Noon, where he wou'd dine with her, and so come home together. She therefore sent a Messenger to tell her treacherous Lover she must needs speak with him on *Thursday* Morning, for she had something of Moment to impart to him; who presently, on the receiving of this Note, came to her, fearing there might be some Discovery of their Love-Enjoyment.

As soon as he was come, she tells him she was extreamly troubled she had not seen him since; and that she never had enjoy'd more pleasure than in his Embraces; and understanding that her Husband wou'd be at home on *Friday* Night, she had contriv'd things so, that he might freely and without interruption lie with her on *Thursday* Night. Which she desir'd on the account of that Affection which she had for him, and of the Pleasure which she took in his Embraces; and that he might be satisfy'd 'twas so, she did engage the next Morning to present him with his fifty Guineas, which she was sorry that she had took of him: and as a further Testimony of it, if he could but procure things necessary for the picking of the Locks belonging to her Husband's Cabinet, she'd give him back the Diamond Ring he gave her Husband as a Pledge for fifty Guineas; and as occasion offer'd, wou'd be very grateful to him otherways.

These Generous Offers overcame the Spark to all intents and purposes; and he would fain have been a dabling with her then; but she forbid him, and told him 'twas not at that time convenient, but she had order'd Matters so, that when he came on *Thursday* Night, there shou'd be nothing to interrupt them. Telling him further, she had made the Maid acquainted with their Secrets, who was intirely in their Interests, and that it wou'd not be amiss to give her something as an Encouragement: and thereupon calling the Maid to fetch a Bottle of Wine, he gave her half a Guinea, and told her, that was but an Earnest of that which he intended her to-Morrow-night. And then drinking his Wine up, he gave his Mistress a Salute, and took his leave; she bidding him be sure not to forget to bring the *Picklocks* with him, that she might help him to the Ring.

The Plot being thus laid, on *Thursday* Morning she prepares to meet her Husband; having before acquainted her Maid with her Design, who mightily commended both her Honesty and Ingenuity; for she knew nothing of what had before past between 'em.

Being come to *Hammersmith*, and meeting with her Husband

there, she told him she had something to say to him privately, that did as much concern his Honour as her own: and then, as they were walking together in the Garden, she thus began to tell him her Design.

My Dear, *I doubt not but you are well satisfied that I have all along took Care in all my Actions still to approve myself* (what you shall ever find me) a chaste and vertuous Wife; *and tho' I am not sensible I ever gave Encouragement to any lustful Eyes to cast a wanton Glance at me, yet so it is, I have been solicited to commit Folly both against Heaven and you, with that young Gentleman, to whom you lent the fifty Guineas on the Diamond Ring; and tho' I have as oft deny'd his Suit as he has made it, yet he continues his Solicitations still; and has been so importunate of late, that I could scarce be ever quiet for him: and therefore being with me yesterday, and urging me for my Consent to his unlawful Amours, I did appoint him to come to me this Night; having before receiv'd your Letter, by which I knew you wou'd be at home. The lustful Fool is extream Confident that I will yield to his Desires; and I thought it best to seem to yield to him, that having caught him in your Trap, you may deal with him as you please. And there's another thing that I have to acquaint you with, and that is, that he's as* Covetous *as he is* Leacherous, *and did but yesterday solicit me to let him have his Ring: and tho'* (to put him off) *I told him 'twas lock'd up in the Cabinet, of which you had the Key: yet he reply'd, he could bring a Pick-lock with him that could open it. So that I am afraid he does design as well to rob you of your Treasure as your Honour. But e're tomorrow morning I hope you'll have it in your power to make him pay for attempting either: at least I have contributed what I can towards it, and leave the rest to you.*

The poor contented *Goldsmith*, (who thought his Wife far shorter than *Diana* of her *Nymphs*; and that the Wife of *Collatine* wa'nt worthy to compare to her) was hugely pleas'd with his *Wife's* Policy, and therefore order'd her to go home first alone, whilst he came after her *Incognito*; and when her Gallant came, he bid her hasten him to Bed, and whilst she stood before him, that the Maid shou'd take away his Sword; and then he thought he might the better deal with a naked Man. All which she promis'd to do.

At Night the poor deluded *Cully* comes to the *Goldsmith's* according to appointment, and was conducted presently up

Stairs; where, that he might the less suspect foul Play, he finds a good Collation provided, which he and his false Mistress feasted at; she urging him to make haste into Bed, that there they might have more *delicious Dainties*; and she beginning to undress her self, he made most haste, and first got into Bed; and then the Maid (as she was before directed) having privately carry'd off the Sword, comes running in upon a sudden, and cries out, *O Mistress, we are all undone! My Master's coming up Stairs.* Up gets the Quaking Beau immediately, and runs under the Bed, which he had but just done, before the *Goldsmith* enter'd: who seeing of his Wife, accosts her thus, *my Dear, I'm come a Day sooner than I expected. – You're very welcome, Love,* said she again, looking as one surpriz'd; at which, cries he, *why how now? What's the matter with you?* And then looking about the Chamber, he sees a very Beau-ish Powder'd Whig; *Ah, ha!* says he, *what have we got here? A Wig new powder'd? Pray whose Wig is this? I'm sure 'tis none of mine;* then looking on the Bed, he sees a pair of Breeches lie; *Hey dey!* cries he, *Pray whose are these? They're yours,* said she, *for ought I know,* (speaking a little surlily) *whose shou'd they be, d'ye think? They're none of mine,* says he, *I'm sure: but let me see, what is there in 'em?* Then searching of the Pockets, he pulls out a Gold Watch, about nine or ten Guineas, a Silver Snuff-Box, and several Pick-locks. As soon as he perceiv'd the Pick-locks, *So, fo,* cries he, *here's a fine Trade indeed! Cou'd you get none to serve you but some Newgate Stallion; one that us'd to Break up Houses, and Pick open Locks! Where is this Villain,* says he, *that wrongs my Bed, and thus dishonours me, that I may run my Sword into his Heart, and send him of an Errand to the Devil?*

The poor dejected Wretch, that look'd each moment to be stuck to the Floor, resolving now to venture on the Goldsmith's Clemency, came trembling out from underneath the Bed, and begg'd of him to save his Life, and he would tell him all that ever he knew. *Don't tell me,* says the Goldsmith, *of what you know, but tell me what Satisfaction I shall have for the Wrong you've done me, to come thus to defile my Bed? Indeed,* said he, *I did it never but once before. How,* says the Goldsmith, *have you lain with my Wife before? Yes, if it please you, once, and never but once.* With that his Wife with open Mouth came to him, *O Villain,* said she, *art not thou asham'd thus falsly to accuse me to*

my Husband, because thy own base wicked Inclinations are now brought to Light? Hast thou not been soliciting of me to act Uncleanness with thee a long time, and I refus'd it always? Nay, didst thou not intice me to it yesterday, and I appointed thee to come to-Night, because I knew my Husband would be at home to Reward thee! Let the Maid speak, I won't be my own Judge – *Yes, Sir,* reply'd the Maid, *I know what my Mistress says is true* –

The Goldsmith then seeming to look more wistly at him, *What, Mr* Bramble, (says he, as if he'd been surpriz'd) *is't you that did intend to claw me off thus? And then to mend the matter, go to accuse my Wife too, as if she had been dishonest with you; when I am satisfied there e'nt an honester Woman in the Kingdom. Why to be plain with ye, 'tis she that has discover'd all your Roguery.* As soon as he heard that, lifting up his Hands and Eyes, *O the Deceit,* said he, *that is in Women!* Pray give me leave to put my Clothes on, and then hear me what I have to say. – *No,* says the Goldsmith, *I will not part with these Clothes; but yet I'll lend you something to cover your Nakedness withal*; and then bid the Maid to reach him an old Suit of his. Which having put on, *Now,* says he, *give me but leave to speak, and I will tell you how false that Woman is*: come, said the Goldsmith, let's hear what you have to say. Upon which *Bramble* thus began.

I must confess my fault; I do acknowledge I did oft times solicite your Wife to let me lie with her, and I must do her that Justice to tell you, that she still refus'd it; until at last I borrow'd fifty Guineas of you on a Ring, and that I gave her, and she thereupon permitted me to lie with her. And I ne'er thought of lying with her more, until she sent for me yesterday morning; and told me how much she lov'd me, and that you were to come home on Friday night, and she wou'd have me lie with her on Thursday night; and that to let me know how well she lik'd me, she wou'd return me back again the fifty Guineas that I gave her, and also give me back the Ring I pawn'd to you for fifty Guineas. And that was the occasion of my coming here to-Night.

But, said the Goldsmith, *pray resolve me one thing; what made you bring the Pick-locks in your Pocket?* I brought these Pick-locks, *reply'd he,* at her desire, to open the Cabinet, wherein the Ring was put.

By that, answer'd the Goldsmith, *I know* that what you have said is false: for *what need she to have desir'd you to bring Pick-locks to open the Cabinet withal, when the Key of it was in her keeping; for I left it with her when I went out of Town.*

'Tis very true, my Dear, *reply'd his Wife,* and here it is. And then going to her Chest of Drawers, she gave him out the Key of the Cabinet.

No, Sirrah, says the Goldsmith, *you're a Rascal; and you accuse my Chaste and Vertuous Wife, because she has discover'd your Baseness: 'tis plain enough that your Design was to debauch my Wife, and then to Rob my House; and I will make your suffer for't, before I have done with you. I have lost above Five hundred Pounds already; and for ought I know you may be the Thief; for I have found you in my Chamber, underneath my Bed, with Pick-locks in your Breeches – Here, Boy, go call a Constable.*

The poor *Beau* finding himself in such bad Circumstances, begg'd him for Heaven's sake, he wou'd not to call a Constable, for if he shou'd be sent to Gaol, his Reputation wou'd be lost for ever. Matters were private now, and if they might be kept so, let him but make his own Demands, and he wou'd satisfie 'em. – This Generous Submission did somewhat qualifie the Goldsmith's Passion. And calling of his Man to fetch his Books up, he look'd what he'd lost by Mr *Thief*; and finding there about four hundred Pounds set down, he told him, *that he'd use him kindly, and take his Bond for Three hundred and fifty pound, including in it the fifty Guineas he had lent him; and for the Ring, since he had in so gross a manner abus'd his Wife he shou'd bestow that on her, to make her satisfaction.*

These were hard Terms, poor *Bramble* thought; but yet considering his Circumstances, he judg'd it was better to comply than go to Gaol, which would be the Result of being had before a Justice.

The Bonds being made and sealed, he fetches him the Ring, which he, (with begging of her Pardon) presents the Goldsmith's Wife, and desire her to accept of it for the affront he so unworthily had put upon her. And then, after a Bottle of Wine at parting, they let him go; restoring him his Cloaths and all things again. She telling of him, as he was going out of doors, *she hop'd that this wou'd be a warning to him how he hereafter went about to put Tricks upon Gentlewomen, or make his Boast what private Favours he had receiv'd from 'em.*

Thus still the Bawd tempts all she can to Sin,
And leaves them in the Lurch, when once they're in.
To heap up Gold, which she so much adores,
She makes Men Atheists, and makes Women Whores.
She lives by Sin; and if she can but gain,
She has her End, let those that list complain.

TWO SONGS

The Sun was just setting, the reaping was done,
And over the Common I tript it alone,
When whom should I meet but young *Dick* of our Town,
Who swore e'er I went I should have a green Gown,
He prest me I stumbl'd, he push't me I tumbl'd,
He kist me I grumbl'd, but still he kist on,
Then rose and went from me as soon as he'd done.
If he be not hamper'd for serving me so
May I be worse rumpled, worse tumbled and jumbled,
Where-ever, where-ever I go.

Before an old Counsel I summon'd the Spark,
And how do you think I was serv'd by his Clark,
He pull'd out his Ink-horn and ask'd me his Fee,
You now shall relate the whole Business quoth he,
He prest me, &c.

The Lawyer then came, and tho' grave was his Look,
Seem'd to wish I would kiss him instead of the Book,
He whisper'd his Clerk then, and leaving the Place,
I was had to his Chamber to open my Case;
He prest me, &c.

Thus *Damon* knock'd at *Celia's* Door,
He sigh'd and begg'd, and wept and swore,
The sign was so, she answer'd No,
No, no, no, no.

Again he sigh'd, again he pray'd,
No Damon, no, I am afraid,
Consider Damon, I'm a Maid,
Consider Damon, no, no, no,
I am a Maid.

At last his sighs and tears made way,
She rose and softly turn'd the Key,
Come in said she, but do not stay,
I may conclude you will be rude,
But if you are you may.

BIBLIOGRAPHY

The size of each work is indicated by the height followed by the width in centimetres, connected by a multiplication sign.

Amusements in high life; or, conjugal infidelities in 1786: in a series of confidential letters, between ladies who have distinguished themselves by the multiplicity and singularity of their amours. London, for G. Lister, 1786. pp. [i] 174. 18×11.

The bon ton magazine; or, microscope of fashion and folly: for the year 1792[–95]. London, W. Locke (vol. I, II), D. Brewman (vol. III–v), 1792–5. vol. I, no. 1–vol. v, no. 60. March 1791–February 1796. pp. [i] 490, [i] 484, [i] 472, [i] 476, [i] 512. pl. 28, 24, 24, 24, 26. 21×12½ (vol. I–III), 22½×13 (vol. IV, v).
The title-pages of vol. I and II both bear the date 1792.

The compleat academy of complements: containing first, choice sentences, with variety of similitudes, and comparisons; also the best complemental letters: second, the art of courtship and general breeding, with discourses proper for this ingenious age, far surpassing any thing of this nature: together with a collection of the newest songs that are sung at court and play-house. London, for E. Tracy and T. Ballard, 1705. pp. [iv] 162. 14×8½.

The cuckold's chronicle; being select trials for adultery, incest, imbecillity, ravishment, etc. London, H. Lemoin, 1793. 2 vol. pp. v 440 (numbered [3] –442), iv 452. 2 front., pl. 12, 10. 20½×12.
BM copy imperfect: vol. I wants front free endpaper and last leaf (a catalogue?) of last gathering; vol. II wants last two leaves (blank?) of last gathering.

[DREUX DU RADIER, JEAN-FRANÇOIS. *Dictionnaire d'amour.*] *The dictionary of love: in which is contained, the explanation of most of the terms used in that language.* London, for R. Griffiths, 1753. pp. xii [226]. 13 × 8.
The original was first published at The Hague in 1741.

The f[ond] mother's garland, composed of several excellent new songs. [Newcastle, *c.* 1770.] pp. 8. 15 × 9.
The title-page of the BM copy is mutilated, the missing letters being placed between brackets in the title above.

Harris's list of Covent-garden ladies: or, man of pleasure's kalender, for the year, 1788: containing the histories and some curious anecdotes of the most celebrated ladies now on the Town, or in keeping, and also many of their keepers. London, for H. Ranger, [1788?] pp. 146. 16½ × 9½.

The history of the human heart; or, the adventures of a young gentleman. London, 'J. Freeman, 1749' [i.e. 1885]. pp. 271. 16½ × 10. Rochester series of reprints, no. iv.
Limited to 100 copies. This work was first issued in 1769 (and reissued by William Dugdale in 1827 and later), under the title: *Memoirs of a man of pleasure; or, the amours, intrigues, and adventures, of Sir Charles Manly.*

The joys of Hymen, or, the conjugal directory: a poem, in three books. London, for D. Davis, 1768. pp. xi [i] 84. 18 × 11.

L., G. *The amorous gallant's tongue tipp'd with golden expressions: or, the art of courtship refined: being the best and newest academy.* Twelfth edition, London, for J. Clarke, etc., 1741. pp. 118. 13½ × 8.
The preface is signed: G.L.

List of the sporting ladies. [London? *c.* 1770.] Single sheet, printed on one side only. 36 × 18.

The London-bawd: with her character and life: discovering the various and subtile intrigues of lewd women. Fourth edition, London, for John Gwillim, 1711. pp. 168+? 14 × 8.
BM copy imperfect: wanting all after p. 168.

'Philosarchus', *pseud.* [i.e. DANIEL MACLAUCHLAN]. *An essay upon improving and adding, to the strength of Great-Britain and Ireland, by fornication, justifying the same from scripture and reason.* By a young clergyman. London, 1735. pp. vi [i] 55. 23 × 17½.

A new Atalantis, for the year one thousand seven hundred and fifty-eight. Second edition, London, M. Thrush, 1758. pp. 192. 16½×9½.

'Philo-Pegasus, a lover of truth', *pseud. Eclipse races, (addressed to the ladies:) being an impartial account of the celestial coursers and their riders, starting together, April 1, 1764, for the Eclipse-plate-prize.* London, sold by J. Whiston, etc., 1764. pp. 24. 25×19.

A riddle: of a paradoxical character of an hairy monster, often found under Holland. Second edition, London, A. Moore, [c. 1725]. pp. 8. 33½× 21.

Satan's harvest home: or the present state of whorecraft, adultery, fornication, procuring, pimping, sodomy, and the game at flatts, (illustrated by an authentick and entertaining story) and other Satanic works, daily propagated in this good Protestant kingdom. London, sold . . . by Dod, etc., 1749. pp. [i] 62. 20×12½.

The trial of wit, or, a new riddle-book: some of which were never before published: composed for the benefit of all those who desire to try their wit, by reading the merry questions and answers. Glasgow, 1782. pp. 24. 14×8½.

[VENETTE, NICOLAS. *Tableau de l'amour considéré dans l'estat du mariage.*] *The pleasures of conjugal-love explain'd: in an essay concerning human generation.* Done from the French, by a physician. London, for P. Meighan, etc., [c. 1740]. pp. [viii] 88. front. 16×9.
The original was first published at Amsterdam in 1687.

Venus unmasked: or, an inquiry into the nature and origin of the passion of love; interspersed with curious and entertaining accounts of several modern amours. London, sold by M. Thrush, 1759. 2 vol. pp. [iv] 120, [i] 112. 14½×9.